To Deo L.

Best ...

[signature]

Ray J Paul was an academic at the London School of Economics and Political Science from 1971 until taking up his professorship at Brunel University in 1992. In December 1999 he diagnosed himself as having Parkinson's disease. He continued working at Brunel University for a further three and a half years before retiring as Dean of the Faculty of Engineering and Information Systems in 2003. Since then he has been a Visiting Professor to both universities, giving advice to staff and PhD students in particular. He is co-editor of an academic journal, and gives seminars at many universities. This book, *Living with Parkinson's disease: Shake, Rattle and Roll* is an honest and open autobiographical account of the author's experiences with Parkinson's disease for 10 years, leavened with black humour vignettes. The story should be helpful to sufferers and carers alike, and is also a good self-help story in its own right. Further autobiographical books based on a variety of his many experiences of life are anticipated.

LIVING WITH PARKINSON'S DISEASE
SHAKE RATTLE AND ROLL

RAY J PAUL

RAIL, London

RAIL

First published in Great Britain in 2009 by RAIL
(Research Analysis Intelligence Limited).
www.rjpbooks.com

Copyright © Ray J Paul, 2009

The moral right of the author has been asserted

ISBN 978-0-9563145-0-5

Printed in the United Kingdom at:
"Islamabad", Raqeem Press,
Tilford, Surrey GU10 2AQ, U.K.

Thank you Jasna

TABLE OF CONTENTS

PREFACE: I'M ILL AND WILL REMAIN SO

In July/August 2003 I wrote some text for myself, recalling the events surrounding my discovery that I had Parkinson's disease: the shock when I realised there was something wrong with me, and what it was. Then there was trauma when I told my wife Jasna, a never-to-be forgotten orgy of despair. I showed the text to some friends and their universal response was that what I had written was very good and I should write the whole story. This is what this book attempts to do, an autobiographical account of me living with Parkinson's disease.

But before telling my story, it seems appropriate that all readers should see for themselves the text I wrote in 2003. Then a similar judgement could be made as to whether you might want to read the book. So if you are browsing in a bookshop or library or a friend's bookshelves, please do read the rest of this preface. And then buy the book please!

Here is the first text I wrote in 2003, amended in the light of only essential updating.

THE 2003 TEXT: THERE'S SOMETHING WRONG

I did not know I was ill. It crept up on me. I was tired in the evenings, and slept or vegetated in front of TV when I returned from work. But the job was demanding. I found physical effort more difficult, but I was out of condition. I had been diagnosed by a doctor as having had a 'funny turn' the previous summer, but nothing more serious emerged as a diagnosis. But at my fathers' 80th birthday party, I knew something was wrong.

The party was held one evening in the last week of December 1999 in the village hall in Tunstall, Suffolk where my father then lived. It was very cold. I delivered a good punchy humorous speech, which whilst gently teasing him, allowed me to publicly acclaim him as a hero to me. I was shaking like a leaf. I explained to the assembled family and friends that I was shaking because the room was cold – but I knew that the temperature was only a minor factor. It could have been nerves – but I knew that was only a minor factor too. So what was going on? I suspected health and determined to investigate.

The next morning, back at home, I looked up 'shaking' – see 'tremors'. There was a long list under 'tremors' which included Parkinson's disease. When I looked the latter up, I was shocked to read a complete description of my physical state as symptoms, and not just temporarily being out-of-condition. I undoubtedly had Parkinson's disease. For example:

I had a stiff shuffling unbalanced walk

An unblinking fixed expression

My walking might turn into uncontrollable tiny running steps

I had a tremor especially on the left side

My handwriting had become very small

My speech was slower and quieter

My movements were very slow

My posture tended to be rigid

Dressing had become increasingly difficult especially buttons

Etc

The medical book was out of date, but it was to be over a month before I was to find out that my life expectancy was only going to be reduced by about 2 years (how would I ever know?) as opposed to one book saying I had 8 to 10 years left.

I waited a few days until 1 January 2000 to tell my wife Jasna. It made sense to me that since we would spend my time in the New Millennium with Parkinson's disease, there was no need to ruin the previous millennium as well. Such is the power of logical thinking when under pressure.

I had been quite calm, even accepting of my fate in those few days when only I knew. But then I told Jasna.

She was completely and absolutely devastated.

We soon sank into masses of joint crying, reading the book again; asking could there be another explanation? There was none.

We had irrevocably set up life together just 10 years before, breaking up both our previous marriages in the process. It had been hard, very hard. Of course finance had been a problem, but the emotional disruption was by far the biggest difficulty. We had managed to upset many friends and family, and of course children, parents and previous spouses were distraught. So were we. After 10 years much of the emotional turmoil had settled down (not forgotten or forgiven though) and we had slowly become materially comfortable. We were looking forward to reaping 10 to 20 years on our investment in each other, and now this.

How unfair!
Why us?
We didn't deserve this!
And so on.

We read more literature, we surfed the Web, we discussed. I had Parkinson's disease, of that there was no doubt.

CONFIRMATION

We had no private medical insurance, but the opportunity arose to quickly get some. Jasna had just changed jobs, moving to my Department at Brunel University. She was being offered a history free membership of a private medical insurance company for herself and her husband as a new member of the University. We jumped at the chance! Why did we bother?

We paid out much more to the insurance company than they did, as annually they remorselessly increased the premiums and reduced the benefits. In the end they paid for nothing for me, not even my two visits each year to my Consultant. We have withdrawn from private health insurance and are investing the money saved each month in savings in case of a future medical need.

With the private insurance 'reassuringly' in place, I went to see the family doctor. I remember offering her my view that I was ill, and I could either tell her what I thought I had, or if she prefers, the symptoms (a previous doctor had made it clear that he made the diagnosis, not me!). She asked me to tell her what I thought I had, and her face drained when I told her. A white-faced doctor was not comforting. She did a physical examination, which whilst she observed she was not an expert, corroborated my view. We sat down to find an expert. She gave me a name and number of a professor, who I phoned when I got home. He did not see private patients. But the secretary gave me the name of a colleague who did, which is how I had the amazing good luck to have Dr Peter Bain, expert on Parkinson's disease, as my consultant.

Within 24 hours I was seeing him and treatment started straight away. I had Parkinson's disease.

I was 52 years old. I had recently been appointed Dean of the Faculty of Science at one of the U.K.'s 130 plus Higher Education institutions, Brunel University. I was line manager to 5 departments, and was doing quite well, as time would show. I had two wonderful grown up children from my first marriage of 19 years. I had a fantastic wife of 10 years standing. We were not poor; we had much respect within and without the University. Life was steadily getting better. What on earth was Mr Parkinson doing, showing up at the wrong party? I had done everything right, so why did it suddenly go wrong? All victims I suspect ask similar questions.

....

Looking back, my diagnosis of Parkinson's disease and the sharing of this knowledge with Jasna, reminds me of the first sighting of the Alien in the film of that name, when the creature emerged emphatically and irrevocably from John Hurt's stomach. Parkinson's disease had been nurturing itself within me at the expense of my brain cells for some indeterminate time, and when it had matured enough, it revealed itself to me and those around me with devastating impact, never to go back on since the cells are lost forever, an effect that would last for life and largely get worse. John Hurt died in the film. I went into bereavement – for myself.

Drafted in 2003. Updated from 2005 onwards

DECLARATION: TRUTH OR FICTION?

I am writing my autobiography as truthfully as I can. To be the truth, I would have to have perfect recall, know exactly what happened to me, and be honest with myself. None of these three requirements are attainable by any human being as far as I know. Some may claim perfect recall, but how can they know if they have forgotten something? To know exactly what has happened assumes there can exist one objective version that everyone could agree to. Even if all the people concerned thought they agreed, how could we know that what each is agreeing to means the same? And honesty with oneself – what tests can you apply to yourself?

So this book is written to the best of my memory, telling my story as I see it now, and trying to be honest. The reader is encouraged to see the big picture. To help understand what I mean by this, those people whose actions might appear not very nice are deliberately not identified. Otherwise they might have disagreed with my account, and of course they may be right. But I do show the way I have seen events, and my view is what makes for the complete story of me. Where possible, I have tried to explain other people's actions from a number of viewpoints, one of which will be mine.

But I repeat, I hope everyone will look at the big picture, an honest attempt to tell the story of how I shake, rattle and roll my life so that I still have as best a life that I can living with Parkinson's disease.

CHAPTER 1

THE ROAD TO PARKINSON'S DISEASE

This book tells my very personal story as a sufferer from the illness popularly known as Parkinson's disease. This chapter provides the necessary scene setting of my life before and just after my diagnosis that I had Parkinson's disease; some of the values I have built up from these experiences which I believe have had some impact on the way I handle my illness; the people in my life, for without them I am not alive (like everyone else); and a road map to the rest of the book. The reader is asked to be patient with this chapter since "you cannot know what I am doing here if you do not know where I came from" (to reverse the usual statement about looking at the future, since for the story in this book the future has arrived).

1.1 WHY DID I WRITE THIS BOOK?

As I have already said in the preface itself, I wrote the preface to this book as a one-off piece of writing in order to express my feelings (as I could remember those three years later), about my discovery that I had Parkinson's disease. I showed the article to some friends and relatives, who expressed surprise and interest in the direct and honest writing. I was encouraged to write about my experiences more extensively and hence this book.

The second reason was to write an account from one Parkinson's disease person to others that they might be able to relate to and hence find helpful. I freely admit that I do not know whether what I have written is unique or even much of a contribution to the literature on the subject. I have read much web-based material, and some Parkinson's Society material. I have also read Michael J. Fox's account of his Parkinson's disease in his excellent book 'Lucky Man' (2002, Ebury Press). Whilst I could relate easily to Fox's story, I feel it is a text that largely enables non-Parkinson's disease people to read to get a feel of what it is like to have Parkinson's disease. But it says little of any personal depth from one Parkinson's disease person to another, as I see it from the intensity and variety of my experience. In this book I attempt an honest and very personal exposition. I found from showing many people early drafts, that this level of honesty makes the book compelling reading for all readers, whether they have an 'interest' in Parkinson's disease or not.

Of course, there is no way I can know how common my personal experiences have been. I am not someone else with Parkinson's disease. I am me. Maybe my experiences have little in common with anyone else. In this case, we shall thereby discover that the effects are extremely varied and individual, an outcome in itself that I would find comforting in that it would teach me to deal with myself on a personal one-off basis. If my experiences have resonance in the Parkinson's disease community, then the book may be helpful in showing that some of the associated physical and mental changes are 'normal'.

The third reason for writing this book is that I had already decided to indulge in some autobiographical book writing (see the appendix on my Seven Autobiographical Books towards the end of the book). Seven books to tell stories about my life – assuming there is sufficient interest in this book to make any more worth writing...

The fourth and final reason is that writing this book might be therapeutic for me. The writing has not proved to be joyous, but the necessary self-reflection has been useful to appraise myself and to deal with life better. And now, dear reader you can comment on my self-appraisal to complete the appraisal activity.

1.2 LIFE BEFORE PARKINSON'S DISEASE

I was born and brought up in East London in the United Kingdom, one of two sons and a daughter. My father Frank Paul was a skilled instrument maker before his only career change, and then he was a sub-postmaster for 50 years. My mother left us all in 1954 to go to Australia to have two more sons and a daughter (my half-siblings, or Ozlings as I affectionately call them). I was then brought up by my Mum, Kathleen Game, who brought her son and daughter (common law step-siblings) to join us in response to an advert my father placed in a newspaper.

I was the first member of my family ever to go to University. I spent six years at Hull University fulfilling everyone's expectation with a first degree in mathematics, and then doing my own thing with a masters and a doctorate in Operational Research.

I became an academic in 1971 when this was the best job I could get due to a slump in the economic cycle. I resolved to take this job until the economy improved, but stayed for life instead. Why? For a number of reasons: an academic is encouraged to think and gets paid as well; the job should be fun - otherwise in my areas of expertise someone can be paid twice as much by some other organisation to be miserable (I have largely had fun in what I have done); I have undertaken part-time consultancy throughout almost the whole of my academic career, in government and commercial organisations, and never once have I been tempted to seek a job in any of these organisations.

Prior to joining Brunel University in 1992, I worked as a Lecturer in Operational Research (1971-87) and then as a Senior Lecturer in Information Systems (1987-92) in the Department of Statistical and Mathematical Sciences at the London School of Economics.

I had been on the professorial appointment circuit for two or three years before success in 1992. Why not wait and get promoted at LSE? LSE appointed a professor in my LSE department in 1986 and then in 2000. There was no indication that I could expect anything in the near future, in fact quite the opposite as my LSE prospects vignette shows.

My Prospects at LSE in 1992 Vignette

Like buses, when I at last got a professorial offer, they came in pairs. Bushy tailed I went to see the Director of LSE and the conversation went something like this:
"Director, I have come to let you make me an offer I can't refuse"
"What do you mean Ray?"
"I have been offered a professorship at South Bank University and at Brunel University. What should I do?"
"Go to Brunel Ray"

I have incorporated similar vignettes throughout the book to lighten up the story. They can be missed out without affecting the story if the reader so wishes.

I joined Brunel University in 1992 as Professor of Simulation Modelling in the Department of Information Systems and Computing (DISC). I was Deputy Head of Department 1992-93 and Head of Department 1993-98. I thought then in 1998 that I would like to go back to full time academic work, but soon had withdrawal symptoms with regard to politics, power, leadership etc. I engineered my appointment as Dean of the Faculty of Science in 1999 (one of 5 faculties), and when the University restructured into three faculties, became Dean of Life Sciences in 2001 for two months and then Dean of Technology and Information Systems until retirement in 2003.

The above paragraph states the facts, but not the experiences, the learning, the struggles etc. These I shall cover fully and insightfully in 'Lucky Ray', one of my other autobiographical books (see Seven Autobiographical Books towards the end of this book). But for now, this précis will suffice for background understanding.

I married Marianne in 1970, a belated school romance leading quickly to a lifetime's commitment. Or so we thought. We parted nearly 20 years later, somewhat acrimoniously at first, more civilized later. What happened? I think what happened is that we set out together, but did not realise we were heading in different directions. Towards the end I mentally decided that it was just a question of time. And this conviction meant I could seek a different future.

In 1988 I met Jasna, and we fell in love, or was it a sickness? It was all-consuming and led to us breaking up both our marriages, after months of lies, cheating and evasion. At the time everyone was made miserable or worse by our totally selfish acts – including us. The feeling of self-disgust was so great that we resolved to try and be honest with each other at all times. It has turned out that such self-honesty has enabled me to face a few years of unpleasantness that I had to endure professionally, as well as Parkinson's disease. On the subject of divorce I offer the following vignette/warning.

My children have been seriously affected, but it is obviously unknown what would have happened otherwise. In the words of Oscar Wilde "First your children love you, then they judge you, and sometimes they forgive you". I have been judged, but luckily after some time I received forgiveness from both my children who were by then mature adults.

> A warning to people intent on divorce vignette
>
> Some of your friends and relatives will take 'sides' and encourage you to 'make sure the bastard doesn't get away with it' and cheerfully tell you how much they have always disliked your partner. If you listen to such 'support' the lawyers will come in and things will get worse. Do not listen to your supporters and do not hire lawyers if you can avoid it.
>
> Marianne and I hired lawyers who did little and of that, much that was harmful. After two years, Marianne and I fired our lawyers, obtained our divorce three months later easily, and six months after that all matters of estate were settled too.
>
> Walk away. Avoid the urge for justice and fairness to prevail. Otherwise you will be consuming your future on your past. There must be something better to do with the rest of your life.

And what have I to say of my first wife, Marianne? Like all of us, especially me, she has her faults and she would be the first to admit to them. And that is where I am going to leave it. There is no need for me to comment, since Marianne can speak for herself. It should be obvious however that I am saying that she is a decent honest woman, but that it did not work out for us. So, after all these upsets, I am extremely fortunate to have my wife Jasna, my son Benjamin, and my daughter Ruth mother of my non-identical grandsons Phoenix and Elliot and my granddaughter Evelyn as my major emotional bedrocks in my life.

1.3 JUST BEFORE DIAGNOSIS

The year 1999 did not seem too good to me. For at least a year leading up to self-diagnosis in December 1999 I seemed to be tired, out of condition, and physical exertion was a problem. It seemed as though I came home from work, started to watch television, and in no time at all, was asleep. My physical movement had taken on what I had thought of as 'cute' characteristics, such as one movement which I later found out was called cog-wheeling. This concerns small movements, which do not happen until with an awareness that no movement is taking place; the small movement is superseded with a more vigorous movement command which then successfully makes the movement. Cute as this might have seemed, it meant that when driving a car, for example, the delicate adjustments to the steering wheel one tends to semi-automatically make to keep the car driving straight, were not being carried out. As the car drifted gently to the left or to the right, a more forceful turn of the wheel would then have to be executed to adjust the car's direction.

Most of this was happening whilst the pressures of work had actually reduced, so from August 1998 when I stood down as Head of Department, until September 1999 when I started my first Deanship, I had no major managerial responsibilities. With the position of Dean coming towards me, in the early summer of 1999 I decided to try and get fit by exercising. I signed up at a local health club, and booked a series of personal assessment meetings with a trainer. During some of the sessions, the trainer noted that my feet were not coordinating at the normal level of harmony. I seemed to have what she called a lazy left foot: that is, when exercising, my lazy left leg does not participate

In the summer of 1999 came a potential severe warning about my health, but the symptoms were not clear enough at that stage to make a diagnosis of Parkinson's disease. But first, I have to make a personal admission. I cannot swim, I have never been able to swim, and I am terrified and convinced it is not for me. I have held this belief since I was a small boy (about 7 or 8 years old) and although Jasna attempted for many years to teach me to swim, my convictions held firm. It was after all a swimming lesson that brought on my health warning in that summer. I have put the story in a vignette called "Panic or Swim".

Swimming at sea even for a Parkinson's sufferer with previous swimming experience might not be possible because of balancing problems and/or small movements required for getting in and out of the sea. And swimming pools have a variety of slippery surfaces that a Parkinson's sufferer might find difficult to negotiate. Swimming is out for me since this incident.

Other health indicators showing the possibility of something being wrong with me included the increasing difficulty I was having climbing the hills/mountains of Acton in West London. You did not know of Acton's hills and mountains? Well, that is because they do not exist! There are some small rises and falls in street level because the land in the area is undulating, but my condition turned these slopes into almost barriers to my movement.

Later in the book I describe the beneficial effect that driving a car has on me, but during the strange period leading up to diagnosis, the purchase of a car also gave clues about what was wrong with me – clues I only recognised as such after the diagnosis.

This one incident in my life where Parkinson's disease impacted on me and my car is in the Car for Ray Vignette.

Looking back and writing the above material shows how easy it is to miss the onset of a slow debilitating disease. Of course all these symptoms match a diagnosis of Parkinson's disease perfectly, but in order to work out what is wrong with oneself, or asking a doctor to do the same, all the 'symptoms' should be recognised as such as they start to emerge and records kept. But who is to know what is a symptom, what is a temporary health idiosyncrasy, what is important and what is not. But at the end of 1999 the diagnosis was made.

1.4 DIAGNOSIS AND TREATMENT

To recap on the story in the Preface: after self-diagnosis at the end of December 1999, I secured private health insurance in January 2000, and then sought medical help from my general practitioner (local doctor). I made an appointment for February 7 2000 with Dr Warren. She responded to my self-diagnosis with visible white-faced shock or surprise as I have already described.

And so I became a private patient of Dr Peter Bain the very next day after all his physical tests confirmed what I already believed to be true. Dr Bain prescribed a Pergolide starter kit with an associated anti-sickness treatment until my body adjusted to the intake of pergolide. Blood tests and an MRI scan showed everything to be more or less normal.

The 'Panic or Swim' Vignette

I was swimming in the sea at Red Island off of Rovinj in Croatia where we were holidaying in the summer of 1999. I had temporarily suspended my beliefs under Jasna's encouragement and was in deep water floating/swimming all of 10 to 20 metres from the rocks at the water's edge. I started to swim towards the rocks, but progress was very slow. I became uncertain and as the rocks seemed to be taking longer and longer to get to, my belief system kicked in – I was going to drown. Then of course, with the onset of panic, I did the complete opposite of what was required and threw my limbs violently in all directions, a method of fulfilling the drowning fear! A mental struggle ensued with one side of the argument telling me to keep calm and to swim to safety and the other side of the argument yelling "I am going to drown". What with the mental conflict and the physical oscillations between thrashing around and making poor swimming strokes, I had no resources left to warn Jasna of my self-inflicted stupidity. I landed eventually – maybe I had been only 3 metres out!

Later that day I collapsed, and Jasna and I struggled to an ambulance station (why didn't we get a taxi!!!) where after some time on a saline drip I appeared to make a full recovery. I was warned that I should seek medical advice about my 'lights' when we returned home, which I did. After a series of tests I was diagnosed as "having had a funny turn". My consultant Dr Bain, when I related this story to him several years later said that diagnosing Parkinson's disease with the level of information I could supply at that time would have been difficult. It was of course in December of that year when I made my own correct diagnosis.

Within a month the anti-sickness pill was deemed unnecessary and the pergolide was at the manufacturers recommended dose of 1 mg three times a day. Physical movement had improved considerably, less sleep was required, but sudden mood swings started, which turned out to be an ominous portent.

The Car for Ray Vignette

I had never owned a brand new car in my life so in the summer of 1999 we decided it was timely and financially feasible to remedy that situation. The car would have to be driven by both of us, especially when we went somewhere together (who is drinking, who is not?) and should be reasonably comfortable. We decided on a Saab, which we both liked, and my old vehicle was also a Saab. Jasna prefers to drive a car with a manual gearbox, so we bought a Saab 9-3 manual, and traded in her Renault Campus car.

I had great difficulty driving the new Saab, or to be exact changing gear. But Jasna could find nothing wrong with the car, and thought the gear change mechanism excellent. It was not until I diagnosed myself with Parkinson's disease in December 1999 that we realised the reasons for my difficulties with the car.

Pressing the clutch pedal to change gear requires an accurate feel for the point of connection and disconnection of the gears as well as the sensitivity to recall the point and go to that point at each gear change. I did not have that sensitivity, I often either did not put enough pressure on the clutch pedal, or what I thought I was doing with my foot was only partially being carried out.

> Once I realised the problem I hated that car. This may or may not be rational, but that was my reaction. After the sorting out of me with medical support and medicines, in the summer of 2003 we went to look for a good second hand car for me. Jasna was delighted with her Saab 9-3. We did not think we could afford two brand new cars in one year.
>
> I still wanted a Saab, so we looked for a reasonably priced second hand Saab 9-5. There were not many on the market.
>
> They ranged from reasonably priced but having done as many miles as my old Saab, to low mileage but almost brand new pricing. And then we saw a brand new Aero which in a month's time was going to be last year's model. And the same car was in another dealers' showroom. After some hard bargaining I secured one of these two great cars at second hand pricing, so not everything in life was bad.

My subsequent treatment is in line with Dr Bain's *Invited Contribution on Parkinson's disease* which follows on from my chapters at the end of the book. So the physical side of Parkinson's disease is normally well under control although there is a frequent need to review and change the medication, and thoughtful monitoring to check on cause and effect. The latter helps Dr Bain revise my prescriptions since when he sees me I can only be in one of a variety of my physical states of well being. The treatment is clearly drugs based. Acupuncture, natural remedies, martial arts, meditation and other methods probably work well for believers in such approaches but I have no difficulty with a drugs based approach if it appears to work, and for me it does.

Although the physical effects of Parkinson's disease were and are well controlled by medication, there have been some major disturbances related to or caused by the disease or the medication. First, I slowly slipped into clinical depression in my first year of treatment, an experience so searing I discuss it in its own chapter, Chapter Two following.

About four years ago in a routine visit to Dr Bain I was asked if I had any chest pains since one of my medications, Pergolide, was being reported as having a side effect on the heart. I said yes, I had an occasional pain under exertion, and with no further ado I was sent to a Rapid Heart Disease unit or some such name, being asked to dress for mild exercise. The visit took four hours with the highlights being as follows. A nurse told me that they wanted to recreate the conditions under which I felt this pain using an exercise bike. I replied I would require a large meal and two glasses of red wine before riding the equivalent of what was a walk up an inclined road from the restaurant to my house. The nurse seemed put out by my response and said I should see the consultant. He suggested I needed a variety of medication and an endoscopy up my groin in the future, but first would I go and do the bike test. Still no meal etc, but I was asked to fill in a waiver form. I read it and asked did this mean that the machine I was going to exercise on to determine the chances of me having a heart attack, might itself give me a heart attack with a 1 in 12000 chance? Although I found the idea somewhat illogical, I signed and off we went. The test went well and my probability of a heart attack was lower than the average for all males of any age. Did I want a copy of the waiver form? I replied to the effect that if I was dead, the form was not much use to me, and if I was alive, what would I do with it? I got the impression that patients do not normally give such replies!

Back to the consultant. My results were so good that the endoscopy was removed from my future requirements. So I was left with a beta blocker prescribed for the heart, a spray if I have a chest pain, and a visit to have a stress echocardiogram. I took the beta blocker for two weeks and then stopped because it was negating the effects of much of my Parkinson's medication, the latter being designed to get me going. I had a stress echocardiogram and I don't recommend it. First an ordinary echocardiogram to set a benchmark was carried out. Then a chemical input that makes the heart race. I was asked by the consultant in charge at one point where I was on a scale of 1 to 10. I should have said 11, but I said 8. That really hurt as more chemical went in. I think it took a week to recover. I asked the operators of the equipment if they had ever undergone the treatment. Oh no, they said, far too intrusive. I agree. But I did get a clean bill of health for my heart.

The latter turns out to be ironic. I would say that I felt my best physically in the summer of 2007, and then it started slipping away. I thought the medication was not strong enough, little thinking that something else could be wrong with me. After all, I had Parkinson's disease, surely that was enough! I continued to decline until in early 2008 an annual blood test showed that the haemoglobin count in my blood was alarmingly low. This would account for the Parkinson's medication not appearing to work – I was too tired for it to be effective.

From that moment, tests produced more bad news so that for a year from 2008 to early 2009 I attended eight different outpatients' clinics looking at all the things that were wrong with me. As well as the blood problem it turned out that my heart was damaged, my lungs had some growth in them etc. The likely culprit was the medication Pergolide, which fortunately anyway Dr Bain had taken the precaution of moving me away from in 2007. I have attended cardiology, gastro-enteritis, haematology, respiratory, and pulmonary heart tension clinics, had endless e.c.g.s, electrocardiograms, scans of all sorts, blood tests to the point of being a pin cushion etc.

The situation at the moment is: the reason for the anaemia is unknown, but iron tablets are at least maintaining the haemoglobin count so I function quite well; the heart, which under pressure was out of balance, is mending; the lung growth is disappearing; there is no obvious problem at the front and end of the digestive system. I have been feeling progressively better for nearly a year now, and this progress still seems to be taking place.

1.5 POST DIAGNOSIS CAREER SYNOPSIS

This section gives a brief description of my professional activities post diagnosis so that the reader understands where everything to do with my Parkinson's disease fits in the coming chapters.

I had diagnosed myself in December 1999, a few months after taking up the post of Dean of the Faculty of Science at Brunel University. I decided not to tell anyone of my illness at that time, and indeed kept it a secret from everyone until I told my family in summer 2002. I then informed friends and professional colleagues in spring 2003. During this time I not only stayed in employment, but took on even more demanding roles. From 2001 to 2003 I was Dean of one of only three 'super-faculties" at Brunel.

As if this were not enough, I was also a candidate for the top job at Brunel, that of Vice Chancellor, in 2001. I resigned in September 2003 when my ideas as Dean were not welcomed by the top management at Brunel, and the political pressures became too great for me. At this time I was probably doing a 150% job, and I knew it was affecting me. So I took retirement and continued to work voluntarily, at a much slower pace.

The wise nature of the decision to retire is evidenced by my looking more and more healthy for the three years following retirement, which shows how debilitating my efforts as Dean had become. My voluntary activities include supervising PhD students, giving advice to all and sundry, and being an editor of an academic journal – oh, and of course, writing books!

The reasons for working or not working, the unpaid nature of my voluntary activity and the decision points in my post-diagnosis existence are part of the material covered in the rest of this book.

1.6 PARKINSON'S DISEASE

Anyone familiar with Parkinson's disease might choose to skip this section, especially as it is deliberately non-technical so that the general reader might appreciate what the illness is without worrying about technical jargon. Having said that I have passed the text by my consultant Dr Peter Bain to be sure I do not mislead. And he has kindly written a proper and extremely helpful and informative medical description of what is known about Parkinson's disease for this book, which I have included in an Invited Contribution section immediately following the main chapters of the book. Read that if you read nothing else. But I am the author of this text and any errors, misinterpretations or lack of clarity are entirely my responsibility.

There is a part of the brain which in conjunction with other parts of the brain controls the physical movement of the body. For reasons not clearly understood yet, in some people the cells in this part of the brain start to die. When about 85% of these cells are dead, then the contribution made to movement control becomes observable – but not before, and by then it is too late. In such people there is no way back, and they have Parkinson's disease.

The part of movement control that is now damaged is that which contributes to delicate precise and slow movements. Keeping your mouth closed for example, which without taking any treatment often produces dibbling from the corners of the mouth. The rate of blinking and hence eyelid movement is reduced which gives the impression that the surrounding facial movements are greatly reduced giving a 'mask-like' effect, or the appearance of expressionless seriousness.

Limbs do not move to order especially for slight movement. Sitting on a chair for most people is landing followed by many slight adjustments so that the position is comfortable. Parkinson's disease sufferers do not make many or any of these slight adjustments on landing or later, until discomfort with the position sets in.

Doing up buttons is extraordinarily difficult since the control needed is slight, precise and rapidly changing as the movement of button entry through to closure goes through a large number of different positions and pressure requirement changes. Non-sufferers need to do a button up very very slowly to appreciate the number of 'continuous steps' they rapidly go through successfully. I give a more exhaustive list of these effects in my coverage of physical movement in chapter 3.

But let me describe an everyday activity to further aid the ordinary reader, the activity of dancing (deliberately selected because this is a source of great personal comfort to me). If the music is fast, and the dance style free form and 'solo' then subject to fitness and an ear for music, a Parkinson's sufferer can dance "quite well". The latter is of course a judgement made by everyone of everyone. I dance like this a lot because this fast free form dancing gives me the feeling for the only time since acquiring Parkinson's disease that I have complete control of all my body, limbs and all. Whether others appreciate my dancing is a matter I guess of their personal well—being since there is no reason for them to object otherwise. I dance anywhere, including on aeroplanes (see vignette Thank You British Airways)!

But the story does not end there, and the following on vignette (*The Thank You British Airways and Virgin Atlantic Postscript Vignette*) shows what has happened since that first sky dancing session.

The Thank You British Airways Vignette

I was on a West Coast to London overnight flight on the business class small upper deck of a Boeing 747. I can tolerate economy aircraft seats for about 2 to 3 hours, otherwise any sponsors of a trip need to find a business ticket for me. But even if I travel in Business class, staying in the seat for too long will 'freeze' my limbs. So, iPod attached I stood near the galley/toilets swaying slightly to some low volume music, and occasionally swapping banter and gossip with any stewardess unfortunate enough to come within charm reach. Observing one of the stewardesses' to be even more sympathetic than the usual high average, I tried out the idea that I might use the galley to more vigorously loosen up. She said yes!

For the next 30 to 50 minutes I occupied about half the galley with the curtain judiciously covering my visibility allowing me to dance at a reasonable pace. During this time other passengers' needs had to be met, so stewardesses would pop in and out of the galley to gather/make refreshments. But these were British Airways stewardesses. Not once did any of them turn a hair that I was there, or disturb me in any way. In fact they behaved as though I wasn't there, some feat considering 50% or so of the galley space. Maybe another airline would have given me the same latitude and in the same style – but anyway, thank you British Airways.

Disclaimer. This story does not suggest that any passenger on a British Airways flight has the right to dance anywhere at all on the plane. My story is not a precedent or policy setter; it is merely a human response to another human's need at a particular time and place and under a set of circumstances never to be exactly matched again.

I am very pleased, and surprised, at how accommodating the crews of these airlines have been. Even in business/upper class there is not always dancing space readily to hand, but every time I have been looked after.

There are certain basic observations to make about dancing at this point in the book, even though because the subject is so fundamental to my life, I give it full coverage in the last chapter. If the music is slow, one ends up incoherently shuffling.

If the dance steps are formal, the chance of getting them right is poor. And close or attached dancing with a partner is difficult, becoming impossible when slow. If I am dancing fast and free and someone stands right in front of me I come to a dead halt.

All my actions are similar. With time, space and speed I am more or less OK. Remove one or more and I rapidly deteriorate in movement ending up with no movement at all. The medication I receive and dancing are mutually supportive, but dancing is no cure.

1.7 WHAT IS TO BE COVERED IN THIS BOOK?

I am not going to tell the happenings and lessons of my Parkinson's disease story chronologically, it would be too boring and not very beneficial.

So I have chosen to present my experiences in useful chunks of material called chapters, each containing a message. But clearly some messages are more important than others, although the ranking will vary from person to person. I am the author, so my decisions on these matters are described below.

The Thank You British Airways and Virgin Atlantic Postscript Vignette

Despite the disclaimer, every intercontinental trip I have made with British Airways (and recently also with Virgin Atlantic) since the above vignette was written has resulted in my dancing during the flight for anything between an hour and four hours. The latter marathon dance activity was for four hours nonstop in the middle of a direct flight from London to Beijing. The crew were so captivated that they gave me a bottle of good wine when we landed which they said was for entertaining them! But that might get them into trouble, so maybe the wine was for filling in a questionnaire.

How do I get permission? I show them these vignettes of course. So it would seem that I have the dancing freedom of the skies. Not quite, many members of the crew then tell me about their personal circumstances and I have to say if a competition was to be run to find the worst of these, my story would be in the tail end of the loser stories - if not last.

I hope the steward who told me his story will not be offended if I mention his awful dilemma some 20 years ago or so when he was diagnosed with cancer of ... Well let's just say, where as a man he would probably least like it. A choice was offered to him whose outcome was obvious since otherwise I would not be writing this. He was worried at the time that his colleagues would find out – they did and they were outstandingly supportive apparently. I am not surprised; I was very impressed with his integrity and bravery.

Chapter 2 describes the clinical depression that hit me for over a year after my diagnosis. The experience is searing, and my description may help those who sink so deep into this awful and terrifying state. Just writing this last sentence brought the tears back, so dreadful was that time. And for those people who confuse unhappiness with depression, my experience may help them understand how lucky they actually are. But my major concluding theme is about the secretiveness with which society handles mental health. I shall explain why this is undesirable, counterproductive if not almost criminal in terms of the treatment received by sufferers.

Chapter 3 looks at the issues and experiences I faced related to all aspects of my physical movement, ranging from: movement when I am on my own; my movement when other people are involved, which can be a mixed blessing; how Society through the State supports the mobility problems of the disabled; the use of a disabled driver's permit to improve access to and from destinations; controls on the licensing of disabled drivers to ensure the safety of both the disabled as well as the public at large; and some summary comments.

Chapter 4 looks at my changes in mental state since I was diagnosed with Parkinson's disease: starting with some easily understandable actions and reactions, including how normal behaviour is often exaggerated by the illness, which can be both a positive and a negative effect; some more unexpected outcomes to do with misuse of sleep etc; some unexpected benefits; changes other people have to make to their view of the world to comprehend any benefits they might gain from interactions with me; the effects on the well-being of my wife and carer; and some reflections on what this all means.

In Chapter 5 I cover peoples' reactions to my illness, starting from my coming out: first with my family; then my friends; then colleagues and acquaintances; new people as I met them, and the current state of affairs. Once I made my Parkinson's disease public, there was a diverse range of reactions. Some people showed themselves to be very immature and/or insecure by the unpleasant way they then dealt with me. At the other extreme I met with an unexpected depth of support, sympathy and love from a mixture of likely and unlikely people (from my view of them previously). Largely, when people know of my illness they express one or more of the following: sympathy, encouragement, understanding, admiration etc.

In Chapter 6 I describe the world of support that someone who is ill like me encounters. Like any service system, the service as it stands has a tendency to become self-absorbing, the increase in communication time rising disproportionately with the number of service employees. I argue for a different approach to service provision. Although many forms of support exist for ill people such as Parkinson's sufferers, the whole collection of support systems assumes normality to be "un-ill", so that someone with an illness is abnormal! The chapter then examines the related issues of working or not, when to make public one's state of health and, my ability to work.

Lastly Chapter 7 is about my passion for dancing and my belief that it should be taken up widely by all who can. This is a mixed chapter, reinforcing the previous 6 chapters. It looks at dancing relative to my needs, its effectiveness, the reactions of people and the complete regaining of control of my body whilst I am dancing.

To conclude this chapter, it is important to know that I have always been an observer of people, who I find extremely interesting. Who needs art galleries and museums when kinetic art is all around us – people? Public places make a backcloth for excellent entertainment as for example, in the American hotel foyer vignette.

The point about this observation, as can be seen from the vignettes already told in this chapter, is that I have a very high awareness of people around me and their activities, and this awareness will make itself felt throughout the book.

As an example, I take the style in which I have written the book. I need to offer solace to those readers who will find my writing style any, many or all of the following: arrogant; pretentious; irritating; self-reflectively self-seeking; self-deprecatingly heroic; and so on. I offer to such readers the observation written in the student yearbook in 1994 at Brunel University:

Professor Paul is unintentionally patronising"!

So, apologies but what you do not like is unintentional. And I hope for all readers my writing style does not detract from the story. The story could probably be told some other way, but it would not be me telling my story. And for most readers of earlier versions of the book, it was me telling the story that was most compelling for them.

The American Hotel Foyer Vignette

In American Hotel Foyers will often find a side table which has fresh coffee, small sodas and something like muffins on it. The table is usually unattended. When someone comes in to the foyer to check in, they hesitate when they see the side table. When the contents of the table start to be apparent to the customers, a broad smile sweeps across their faces. Now fully alert, they quickly check around them to see if there is some control of the table or if anyone is watching them, and now with a look of suspicion replacing the smile. No controls, yummy - time to move in on the kill. At the side table, a quick suspicious glance back around the foyer, no control, so then with a very broad smile the check-in person clutches 50c worth of cookies and one of America's barely drinkable sodas. And now, big smile still, each prize-winner is ready to check-in to a $200 a night room.

CHAPTER 2

DESPAIR AND BACK? – SHAKE AND RATTLE

In this chapter I describe what happened to me as I went into clinical depression during the first year of my treatment for Parkinson's disease. As well as a fairly honest account of my personal trauma I also discuss the way as a Society we deal with all forms of mental illness, or rather how we do not deal with it. This is so counterproductive for everyone I make a plea at the end of the chapter for more openness about the issues.

For those readers who have suffered clinical depression the third section describing my personal suffering will have immediate parallels for them. For readers who have fortunately avoided this condition so far, my description is an understatement of just how awful the illness can be – no mere words are sufficient to convey the effects.

2.1 EARLY IMPACTS ON ME AND TREATMENT

Obviously having any incurable illness has some sort of mental impact on the sufferer: the knowledge that there is no cure in itself is hardly a cause for great optimism. However there is a world of difference about being unhappy with your situation, or even depressed using the latter word in its everyday usage, and the state of clinical depression. Ordinary unhappiness or depression is about being your normal self, but not being very happy with your circumstances. Clinical depression is where you become another person, completely in the control of the condition, hardly if at all capable of understanding what is happening to you, and not capable of taking any steps to get out of the situation. Someone with clinical depression is so constantly mournful that non-sufferers commonly exhort the sufferer to 'buck up' or 'cheer up' or 'try harder', all phrases that make the sufferer feel worse, since the implication is that the sufferer is in their state by choice, and could with a good shaking just come out of it. If only it was that simple.

There is no automatic connection between Parkinson's disease and clinical depression; over half of Parkinson's sufferers do not suffer from clinical depression after all. But the minority who do is estimated to be as high as 40%. And I was one of these 40%. I have tried to convey the experience in the third section but it is almost impossible to explain to someone who has not had clinical depression just what the state is like. But I hope I manage to convey in this chapter the uniqueness of the state of clinical depression. And how to treat it? This will only improve when such illnesses are accepted as part of the human condition and we start to accept them in everyday life. At the moment, the usual reaction to such illnesses is a logical discussion by non-sufferes about a remedy, without any understanding that the sufferer has a completely different view of the world in which everyday logic plays no part at all.

So, this chapter is about the mental effects, what I have so far referred to as my mood swings but which rapidly degenerated into clinical depression, probably the worst experience of my whole life. This is not an easy story to tell, partly because society keeps any form of mental illness quiet – an attitude that with my personal experience I find ridiculous and counter-productive. Because of course, this was a particularly powerful experience for me. The chapter looks in the next section at some of the reasons for being clinically depressed and what this means for sufferers before describing my personal experiences as clearly as I can. The way back from clinical depression via medicine, self-help and my carers is covered in the fourth and fifth sections followed by a penultimate section on discussing honestly and openly one's situation in public. The chapter ends on a call to Society for mental illness to be treated openly like any form of illness.

2.2 You're in Bereavement – You Think You've Died

Like anyone else I have been happy, unhappy and so-called depressed in a variety of ways throughout my life. When I was low I might say I was 'depressed' without a proper understanding of the significance of the term. My clinical depression took off in 2000 and was eventually controlled but not before the end of 2001. Being clinically depressed was something I could never have imagined prior to the experience and like other sufferers I find it is almost impossible to explain to non-sufferers what it was like and why I suffered from it. One explanation of why I became clinically depressed was suggested by my local doctor Dr Warren who said, it was as if I was in full-scale bereavement – and the person I was bereaving for was me! The diagnosis that I had Parkinson's disease was though I had been told I was dead.

A large minority of Parkinson's sufferers suffer partial or full clinical depression but there is no known causal link. First I shall offer some thoughts on causes before introducing an excellent book on the subject of depression, which is fairly comprehensive in its coverage of all the aspects that sufferers of depression and their carers need to know. But first why did I sink into such despair that I became clinically depressed? I have no idea but I have obviously given some thought to this and I have come up with the following (probably non-exhaustive) collection of explanations.

First, maybe I was always a latent depressive and my illness tipped the balance. I expect anyone reading a list of characteristics and behaviours of victims of depression will see parts of themselves in such lists. And that is because such lists do not distinguish 'neutral' and 'depression' symptoms, since such distinctions do not exist. It is the combinations of characteristics and behaviours that determine the distinction, and I suspect at that point the result is self-evident anyway (to the professionals). So I can read such lists and see myself as a depressive person. Or not.

Second, maybe I as an individual could not handle the situation, the bereavement scenario. Traumatic experiences such as bereavement are known to at least tip the mental balance if not be the cause of the depression in many cases. I do not know whether bereavement is an accurate description of the cause(s) of my depression, but I was certainly not too pleased with the confirmation that (as an Economist might say) in the long run we shall all be dead, including me.

Third, maybe one of the associated characteristics of some forms of Parkinson's disease is depression. My consultant calls my condition Parkinsonism because it has become accepted that rather than there being just one illness called Parkinson's disease (which would suggest uniformity of impact and even possibly of treatments), there exists a family of similar diseases with much in common but with distinguishing features between them and other members of the Parkinson's disease family. I am not aware of the distinctions, but maybe one branch of the family has a set of circumstances that inevitably cause depression and maybe my illness fits into such a branch.

Fourth, maybe the medicine induced depression. I take a lot of medicine. They have all been tested. But I doubt my exact combination of medication has been tested against a non-depressed patient with exactly the same medication. In fact with 10 different medications, the chances of doing this are very slim. So no one can be sure that a combination of pills will or will not induce depression. And nor do I know why I haven't got depression now, although it is a constant fear that it will return, especially.

I have been liable to mood swings from day to day, although these have been fewer with the passage of time. As part of my fight against depression I read Lewis Wolpert's book Wolpert L. Malignant Sadness The Anatomy of Depression, 2nd edn. London: Faber, 2001. Wolpert is a Professor of Biology at University College London. At the time I read the book in 2000 it was still in its initial edition and Wolpert had had one attack of depression. This was very severe as can be easily determined from the opening sentences of the book:

"It was the worst experience of my life. More terrible even than watching my wife die of cancer." (Wolpert, 1999).

These amazingly powerful sentences remain as the opening sentences to both the second and third editions. I found the book so informative and helpful that I buy multiple copies (10 to 20 at a time) to give away to the many people affected by depression. I needed and received help with my depression, so it is only reasonable that I help as I can in this way. I will talk more about the impact of depression on the population at large near the end of this chapter.

I do not intend to reproduce Wolpert's book in this, my book. I have my own story to tell, and Wolpert's book is so compulsive that everyone affected by depression as a patient or carer should read it (which is probably most of the population). Wolpert covers the history, the definitions, and current knowledge and diagnosing techniques. The latter can be unbelievably primitive, a list of possible symptoms which when checked off result in a diagnosis of depression if the score is high enough (say 16 out of 24) and not otherwise!!

Wolpert makes several pleas for improvement to the treatment of the clinically depressed, including the observation that not prescribing anti-depressant drugs where they would assist should be regarded as a criminal act. The book also covers what it feels like to be depressed, whilst making the observation that I made earlier, that it is impossible to convey what depression is to the fortunate uninitiated. I leave the reader to find out more of what is in Wolpert's book, whilst in this book I relate my personal experiences.

In the third edition of his book Wolpert makes the observation that because when people are unhappy they describe their state as depressed, this is confusing when the same word is applied to the clinically depressed. Such confusion can lead to the innocent "pull yourself together" statement to someone who is unhappy being used on a clinically depressed person. In the latter case the use of such 'buck yourself up' language reinforces the depression for reasons that will become more apparent in the next section. So Wolpert suggests that maybe we need some distinction between the cases and hence a new word to describe one or the other. Since depression is widely used by the population at large, a new word for clinical depression might be the answer. But which word?

I shall attempt to find such a word at this point in my text, not because I expect any suggestion I make to be universally adopted, but because the reasoning behind the consideration of one word or another in itself provides insight into the nature of clinical depression for the fortunate uninitiated. There are a number of ways one could go about finding a new word. For example Table 1 shows lists of words: the first list concerning words that are to do with clinical depression (for example, extinction is a prospect facing someone at the bottom of their depression); the second list is of words that having the same ending as the word 'depression'. The third list is of words that are opposites to the world the depressant faces (which is of no ambition, no intent etc).

Table 1. Lists of words associated with the word 'depression', or with the same root, or having an opposite meaning

Words associated with clinical depression	Words with the same root as depression	Negative expressions of clinical depression
Bleak	Expression	Ambition
Dead	Impression	Desire
Deathly	Oppression	Ecstatic
Despair	Repression	Future
Dishearten		Intent
Extinction		
Failure		
Fear		
Melancholy		
Miserable		
Misery		

Table 1 then allows various forms of new word creation. For example using the word ending as a basis you get Table 2, where the word ending for the word 'depression' is used with the first part of any appropriate word in order to create a new word. I quite like the look of "Mispression". Table 3 shows some possibilities from changing a synonym of the word depressed, of which there are many in Table 1 (column 1), or an opposite word (column 3).

My favourite at the moment is 'Deheart' or 'Dehearten', a word I made up from the word 'dishearten'. Dishearten means something like: to make somebody lose hope and enthusiasm. So 'dehearten' or 'deheart' could be used to mean: when somebody loses hope in themselves and any enthusiasm

Table 4 gives two possible constructs based on the word dishearten. My favourite is deheart since its various forms seem easier to say to me.

Table 2. New words for the clinical variety of depression formed from the second part of the word 'depression' combined with the first part of a similar word.

New word ending in ~pression	Word that gives the start of the new word
Apression Appression	Approaching the bottom
Basepression	
Bleakpression Bleapression Blepresssion	Everything looks bleak
Clinpression	Clinical depression
Deathpression	Death is a major source of mental activity when depressed
Deeppression	
Deepression	Deep depression
Despression	Despair, how the depressed feel
Diepression	Die

53

Fatalpression	
Fearpression	Fear, obviously part of depression
Melapression Melancolpression Melpression	Melancholy
Mispression	Misery, miserable
Nilpression	Etc; etc
Nohopepression	
Nonepression	
Nopression	
Nullpression	

Table 3. New words for clinical depression formed from similar or opposite words to depression

Synonym or antonym root	New word for depression
Didhearten	Deheart Dehearten
Ecstatic	Destatic Misestatic Nonestatic Unestatic
Melancholy	Deepmelancholy

But the main point for the reader who has looked at all this word play is to get a better feel for the nature of clinical depression or deheart from the words that have been considered in this exercise.

Table 4. Two alternatives dehearten and deheart, of a new word for clinical depression based on a variation of the word dishearten

The current word for depression in all its forms	A new word based on the word dishearten	A new word based on the idea of the word dishearten shortened to deheart
Depressant	Deheartenant	Deheartant
Depressed	Deheartened	Dehearted
Depressing	Deheartening	Dehearting
Depression	Dehearten	Deheart
Depressive	Deheartenive	Deheartive
Depressor	Deheartenor	Deheartor
To depress	To dehearten	To deheart

2.3 CLINICAL DEPRESSION – NO EXPERIENCE LIKE IT

Everyone dies, apparently. I must admit a variety of thoughts concerning death had been entertained by me over the course of my lifetime. Such thoughts were allowable since unfortunately I have no religious beliefs. I say unfortunate because with belief comes the afterlife. I have no sure future to look forward to. As far as I can see, when you are dead, that's it. But the world only exists because I do, would be a typical musing of mine. That is, what I know of the world is processed by sensory devices and made sense of by my thought processes. Remove me, and none of this happens, so clearly for the world to exist, so must I. Admittedly this simple logic fails when considering what was happening before I was born. If nothing, then everything is just fantasy, and therefore so am I. But if the world existed before my birth, then it is possible to continue in existence after my death. Clearly there is something wrong with this – isn't there?

Or, to put it another way, I agree with Woody Allen when he said "I don't want to be immortal because of the words I wrote, I want to be immortal because I didn't die!"

With my diagnosis of Parkinson's disease came the awful realisation that I was going to die too. Hence the appropriateness of my doctor's description of me bereaving for me. But as I mentioned above, the cause(s) of my depression are uncertain. There is little data, no parallel worlds to experiment with, and a host of models from the sciences and social sciences that would fit the sparse data to the satisfaction of the researcher(s). As a modeller myself, I have come to see model-to-data- fit to be yet another potential misuse of modelling.

I sank mentally in parallel with a weight loss of 1kg a month for a year. At first it was mood swings, but the swings became deeper and deeper, heading down more and more and less and less up. After 3 to 4 months I was clinically depressed, which has come to mean for me the following awful experience.

At the darkest depth, nothing and no one matters including oneself. Especially oneself. And it's not that you wish you were dead, which would be bad enough. At the depths of my clinical depression every part of you, physically and mentally wanted to die. All my senses, all my internal communications, my brain had one simple message for me – die. Not only did nothing else matter, nothing else was considered. Time after time I lay on a bed crying uncontrollably wanting to die, to be dead. On some occasions a band of steel was clamped tightly around my upper torso, so realistically that sometimes I even felt my body for it even though I knew it wasn't there. These were extraordinary experiences for me; all parts of me were in complete agreement amongst themselves that I should be dead, that the only thing to do as far as the future was concerned was kill myself as soon as possible. The desire to be dead was relentless. Wherever I was, if I was not fully mentally occupied, a black cloud of death would descend, envelop, soak into me and as one, the only menu, the only future the only purpose of existence was death.

Jasna and I went on holiday in summer 2000, just after my depression was around its lowest. Most days we would take a 30-minute journey to a small island off the Croatia Coast near Dubrovnik to enjoy naturist beaches with clean water and plenty of space. And then the black cloud would descend, at different speeds on different days and we would have to make our way back by the next small ferry boat to the hotel room, there to lie crying and wishing to be dead. That is, if we ever got out of the hotel room that day at all.

And the speed of descent could also be astonishing, sometimes like going into freefall. I liken it to an aeroplane I was once on which hit turbulence just before landing at Ljubljana, Slovenia. Every now and then the plane seemed powerless and just fell out of the sky heading for the ground still horizontal but at an amazing speed. Everyone on the plane, passengers and crew, was terrified including me – or especially me! The analogy is imperfect however because on the aeroplane I wanted to live. In a depression freefall, crashing and dying would have seemed perfect.

In general my interest in the world more or less ceased. I stopped watching television, both because it was too slow for me (my Parkinson's medication made me generally more lively, including my mental speed) and because this then allowed me too much slack thinking time which easily concentrated on matters about myself and hence the possibility of sinking. Similarly for newspapers. Fortunately with an increased mental speed came the ability to pick up what is going on in the outside world from snippets of TV and radio output that I heard as well in conversation with others. I could read if the material was about ideas, ideas that would absorb my interest.

What did I do about my dehearted state? The next section discusses my path out of the depths.

2.4 MEDICATION AND BE NOT IDLE

Even when lying on a bed weeping and everything telling me to die, my brain, which tends to look at my world as a set of systems, was looking at my state and declaring that something was wrong. If everything was telling me to die, then what made my current situation any different from my situation before I had clinical depression? And I had not wanted to die before. So why this change? So whilst the death wish was my dominant feeling, my mental processes allowed me to stand back from the situation, see that nothing much had changed, that my situation was not particularly different to other people (many people have far more serious illnesses than mine), and to declare that my desire to die was obviously in error. Such thinking did not ease the black pain, but it gave me the opportunity to think of ways of escaping.

Since medicine had done so well for my Parkinson's disease, it was natural for me to use medication to help me. I do not advocate medication above other approaches, it just happens to suit me. I do not think this means it suits everyone else. By the same logic, if someone else has another route to getting out of the depths, it is not acceptable to me to be told that this is the method I should use also.

Having said that, drugs are tapping at the surface of depression, somewhat in a hit and miss style. When I took antidepressants in 2000 and 2001 it took several attempts to find one that worked on me. In the meantime, down I went. And when you have found one that works, it can take some time to wean oneself off it, so it wasn't until early 2002 that I stopped taking antidepressants. On the other hand, the drugs available are improving rapidly.

The other problem with drugs is the side effects. I once heard, second-hand, that a psychiatrist had observed that using antidepressants was similar to lighting an office with difficulties in a skyscraper. That is, in this case, the only way to switch the lights on in one room was to switch all the lights on in the whole building. In antidepressant terms, one may know the effect on depression, but what else about you that is affected remains to be a learning experience. I was very pleased after having tried one drug for six weeks, we moved to another. The first drugs made me sweat more – with an evil odour. Waking up in the morning was accompanied by an immediate desire to get away from one's own body, so appalling was the smell!

But drugs worked for me, and if they can help, they should be offered, since staying in depression is unbearable.

Apart from drugs, I also attempted to not think about my condition as much as possible (difficult when a skunk would avoid meeting you). Work helped. I have always had a Chinese Walls approach to my professional life in that it is completely divorced from my private life. In my professional life I see every activity as a game, a game to be played to win maybe, but win or lose is not life. This is the systems thinking at work again, looking at every situation as a system, modelling it as a game, and then trying to improve the game outcomes. This turns out to be helpful to other people as well, so I have from a very early time in my career been sought out for advice (more on this later). Which means my natural predilection to interact directly has been increasingly satisfied by my career. So when I was in depression, I could go to work (usually late, getting out of the house was not easy, and never has been since) and my mind would be fully occupied with non-stop interaction with an endless queue of appointments, meetings and droppers-by. If meetings were boring I had developed a range of methods to liven them up and move them on, or I would systemically analyse what we were up to and probably generate some more 'rules of life' to add to my collection (soon to be a book also).

So at work I had no 'time' to be depressed, I had no time to think about me. And then I would go home, lie on the bed and want to die. How can anyone who has never experienced this ever understand it?

One correction I must make, and that there is one topic in my professional career that has never been a game and which I have always taken quite seriously. But I have addressed the issue through the use of other games of course. And what is this topic of such importance?

My salary of course.

The business of being occupied mentally is something Wolpert spends a lot of time on in his book, and I can only concur with everything he says. Memorably his book ends with a sentence that for different reasons is as resoundingly striking as his opening sentence, mentioned above. And the sentence is:

Be Not Idle

I can only reinforce this view; a depressive should never be idle, because that provides an opportunity to sink. To get off or keep off the bed with its accompanying copious weeping, I went as far as sorting screws. I have always had a toolkit for DIY, where my ambitions and outputs throughout time have never met. I added to this rapidly. I now believe it to be a sub-conscious attempt to ward off the evil time when Parkinson's disease might make me too immobile to use tools, by stocking up and doing as much with them as possible now. During my depression I frequently spent 2 to 4 hours in my shed, resorting, rearranging and changing the layout of the shed and the tools. And sorting screws was a major part of this. Now when I proudly show visitors the end results, what they see is an anally retentive tidiness out of all proportion to any needs.

But it kept me going.

There is one more major ingredient in my struggle to throw off my 'Black Dog' (which is apparently what Winston Churchill called his life long struggle with depression – Anthony Storr, 1999, Churchill's Black Dog, Harper Collins). My carers. This is such a major element of any depressant's struggle; I am spending the next section on it in its own rights.

2.5 THE CARER SUFFERS MOST

The title of this section may appear a little unlikely, or maybe pandering for a need to be grateful for what has been done for me. I shall cover the issue of my carers both for Parkinson's disease and for clinical depression.

First of course, there are the professional carers, the doctors and paramedics, my Parkinson's disease consultant and so on. Obviously they have been an important part of my diagnosis and treatment; in fact I would not be writing this book if it were not for the excellent support they have given me, enabling me to function as well as I do. But I do not think they have suffered, at least I hope not. My consultant always seems pleased to see me because he tells me I am doing so well. All the professional carers have to extract themselves from my natural tendency with almost anyone to examine new things, discuss life and be the recipient of the advice I generally distribute wanted or not. Appointment schedules are easily ruined by my inclusion in one. Maybe they suffer from this, but this is not the level of concern that this section is about.

Because of Parkinson's disease, and my fear that declaring it might mean the end of my career (discussed in detail in chapter 6), I only had one carer during my depression, and the reality is I have had one overwhelmingly major carer all the time. My wife Jasna. Jasna saw me weeping on the bed, was dragged off beaches, saw my fears before appointments with the professionals, watched my anxieties and still has to handle a potentially anxious, moody, unreliable, messy, self-absorbed and basically demanding individual more or less full time and from the beginning when I told her of my Parkinson's disease suspicions on 1 January 2000.

Whilst I suffered and fought for amelioration, she suffered too (as one does when your loved one is in pain), but she could not seek meaningful remedies since she could not fully understand my state (fortunately, since this would have required her to experience it herself). She has coped amazingly well, but at a cost. I will come back to the latter later in this section, but let me give you idea of what she has to handle and how she has coped.

In the depths of depression I investigated how to get out. As a computing academic, obviously searching the web would be the approach to take. I surfed. Since I am not a proponent of suicide, I will not tell you what I found. But one day Jasna "caught" me. I have described the essence of the event in the Suicidal Vignette below. I have highlighted it in this way because I think it contains a universal truth for all depressants or suicide candidates. And that is, you may not find life worth living; you may not even have the emotional energy left to know whether you love or even care for anyone else. But someone loves you, probably many people. And they want to help. But they need to know what the problem is and be allowed to give support. And they need you. Suicide may appear to offer a solution to your pain (hardly a solution though), but if you go through with it, you will leave behind unimaginable pain (unless you experienced it from someone else).

The motivation to hang on is quite simply to care for the people who love you. Stay alive for the people who love you even if you cannot stay alive for yourself.

There is a dilemma in the carer/cared for relationship. If I were to tell Jasna all the mental pain I feel, it would overwhelm her. As it is she knows there is a problem when my eyes go 'black' as she calls it. But if I do not tell her she feels excluded. I attempt to get a sensible balance about this, whatever that means.

Because I appear to successfully handle most of my illness problems, especially lately, she would prefer to believe that I am well. On balance I prefer that; there is no benefit for me in being treated like a permanent invalid. But this means I will be found wanting quite frequently on matters that I could have handled before my illness. And then I often resent being addressed on the issue. Surely with all my heroism in fighting my illness so well, I do not deserve to be so unsympathetically treated? So there is a tension on and off between us, where I try and behave the way she would like, and she tries to behave the way that I would like, and this then ends up upsetting us both.

And what of the effect on her? I am guessing, but I think what has happened is the following. First my Parkinson's disease and then clinical depression made her appreciate the frailty of life. Looking after me did not persuade her that being not healthy had any advantages.

Suicidal Vignette

I had no purpose in life, I wanted to die – overwhelmingly so at times. How do you kill yourself though? Horribly horribly seemed an unnecessary extra to what was meant to be an end of suffering.

I surfed the web. Jasna caught me – did I intend her to? Possibly, probably, to this day I am not sure. What did I expect from her – sympathy, reassurance etc? I cannot tell you exactly what she said, but it was emotional, powerful and something like:

"You selfish bastard. You don't care for me at all. Here you are, thinking only of yourself, taking the easy way out, not caring that you will leave me alone with no future without you. You can't love me if you do this, how could you?"

Jasna's reaction was a complete surprise to me, and if I had known what it was likely to be, I would have judged that it would have made me worse.

Wrong. Jasna' reaction jolted me out of my "Number One First" worldview and reminded me forcefully that being alive is not just about oneself. In fact without others to consider, life might then become intolerable. I had got the chicken and egg in the wrong sequence – as if I knew which is which anyway!

So whilst she has always looked after herself physically, both in terms of health and also appearance, she now pursues these activities with a vengeance. Holidays at the seaside can become Amazonian trials of swimming performance – if the sea temperature is not too low! Domestically she has taken up tennis since 2003, and now pursues that with such hunger I can't help the feeling that if she had started tennis in her youth she might have been a Wimbledon star.

Hairdressers, beauticians, health food, and food supplements, the need to look and feel young and healthy – these are all things people pursue at one level or another, but rarely with such passion. And this I believe to be her escape from the relentless reminder of my condition. It will be no surprise to hear that like all ill people, every day when I wake up reminds me of my Parkinson's disease. It may be more surprising to know that every day when Jasna wakes up, she reminds herself of my Parkinson's disease. The difference between us is I can see ways of handling my circumstances, with increasing success, whilst she is more than willing but helpless to do similar for me.

And for all that she does for me, she is likely to find my gratitude expressed in terms of what she is not doing for me: the allowances she is not making for my illness; how she nags too much; how she spends too much time on herself. Why she puts up with me I have no idea. She says it is because she loves me. She must do!

Some of my solutions for dealing with myself may sound interesting and to be congratulated by the neutral observer. You try living with them. My passion for dancing and music means that I often walk in public places with an iPod attached firmly to my ears, or when visiting or being visited, and the need arises during the visit, excuse myself from the company on the grounds that I need to dance. The latter I am happy to do in front of company or in another room or garden, I don't mind.

People are very gracious and do not appear as though this is anything other than normal behaviour. But imagine you were Jasna and your partner was likely to break into a mute song and dance act at any time.

I have the health problems, I can work out what I need to address. If an approach does not work I can try something else, when it works I feel good. Jasna has my symptoms as a problem second-hand, cannot know what will work because she has no personal experience, would feel a failure when an approach she persuades me to follow does not work, and will probably see me getting all the credit for something that did work.

I suffer, but Jasna suffers most of my disadvantages, and few of my advantages. I can help myself; she is largely aching to help me and is very frustrated she cannot. It depends on the kind of person you are I suppose; but it seems to me Jasna has suffered more than me although differently.

2.6 SECRECY, OPENNESS AND PROSELYTISING

I have already mentioned that I was unwilling to tell anyone about my Parkinson's disease in case my job was affected. When I went open in 2003, then I could talk about clinical depression as well. By then I was already of the view that the way in which our society in general largely hides mental illness as though it was a stigma, an embarrassment, was not only morally and ethically wrong, but counterproductive to sufferers, professionals and society at large. In other words everyone. So I decided to be open and honest about my depression as an example. What this led to I describe in this section.

First, people were quite surprised that I of all people had ever had a depressed moment in my life, so good had I become at cheering up people and solving their problems. No one had noticed anything amiss during my depressed period other than the fact I lost considerable weight. And then there was some surprise that I was willing to talk about my experience, but never any question as to my integrity or mental capacity. Such conversations were held privately of course and it is as a by-product from doing such a series of such conversations that the full stupidity of our society's approach to mental illness became clear.

I had already read (Wolpert I think) that one third of the population would suffer clinical depression at least once in their lives. I had subconsciously assumed that most of the other two-thirds would encounter some aspects by servicing the needs of the sufferers. But these were bare statistics. Since 2003 I have had the following sets of experiences.

First. As I have related my story the listener has suddenly burst into tears in front of me. They were or had been clinically depressed. Outside of their immediate family they had never discussed the subject, and they had never met someone else doing so either. My openness shook them, touched them and opened them up in their turn. Their story poured out to someone who had admitted his experience, been openly honest about it, was knowledgeably sympathetic, would keep a trust and was willing to help. Their stories were often much worse than mine and although there was little to nothing I could do to help them (usually to give or send them a copy of Wolpert's book), they found great comfort in relating their experience to a knowledgeable co-sufferer. Keeping mental illness a secret means that it can be quite common for sufferers never to talk to another sufferer, to share experiences and learn from each other. With mental illness shared experience is more essential than for any other sort of illness I would guess.

Second. Many co-sufferers did not break down in front of me, but slowly they would feed me enough clues to allow me to determine their situation and when I was reasonably confident, I would ask the direct question to which they all responded with agreement and then their stories would pour out.

Third. Many people had or were looking after sufferers and had rarely spoken about this to anyone. Whilst not fully understanding the nature of the illness they had been caring for, they were immensely pleased to be able to talk to an open and honest ex-sufferer to see if some of the questions they had could be answered and to have a chance to try out their views on their experiences.

Fourth. Some people I have met I realise are probably depressed or on their way. When I try and tease this out of them, they inevitably become defensive. This is not a subject to talk about further, and I was prying. So I would explain that I was not insinuating anything about them, it's just that some of the things they had said or written or reacted to reminded me of when I had been depressed. And then I would tell them my story. At some point they would interrupt, admit their state and of we would go into discussion. Such people were invariably not being cared for, and my advice, concern and insistence of their situation being 100% no-blame seemed to be very helpful.

Many I have successfully persuaded to seek the professional advice they badly need.

Fifth. Some people open up to talk about their fears for a loved one. As we discuss the possible sufferer it is often quite clear that the person I am talking to and the sufferer are not only fairly ignorant of what they are dealing with, but are taking unhelpful actions.

What do all these discussions have in common? Lack of discussions about depression leads on to fear, worse depression, poor support and general pariah status

So far I have described my openness and provision of advice to clinical depressive people or their carers. But I have had other experiences of mental illness in my lifetime, and I am now going to move the call for openness onto a wider appeal discussed later, with these stories providing more ammunition.

2.7 A Plea for Mental Illness to be Handled Openly

Whilst this book is clearly declared to be an experiential offering by the author to the reader, this section is more of an opinion piece. I have no medical expertise of any kind. I do not even claim to be an evidenced based amateur. I give limited advice to those dealing with clinical depression based on my one-off personal experience. Maybe my ignorance is such that I should refrain from doing even this. But I do consider myself to be fairly good at looking at the world around me as systems at different levels. The expertise one can acquire in looking at the world as systems is to determine at what level of detail to describe anything as a system, and within that level, what the causes and effects might be.

Then determine the feedback mechanisms in the system. one is in a position to look for system improvement. It is in this latter spirit that I offer my opinions in this section.

Nearly everyone suffers from illness at various times during their lives and if the illness is physical, this is an acceptable topic of conversation. If the illness is mental however, this is widely regarded not to be an acceptable topic of conversation. One can hypothesise many reasons for this, including fear, public humiliation, or the relative inability of the sufferer to articulate their illness as readily as they could for a physical illness. But whatever reason(s) one chooses, the plain fact is that the most complicated part of our anatomy is the brain and the neural system, so much so that it would be reasonable to expect some malfunction of these during one's lifetime relatively to physical malfunctioning. But this complexity is as yet little understood compared to the more obviously viewable and measurable physical illnesses. That is not to say that professionals in the mental illness arena are not doing well, but that our ignorance about the cause and cures of mental illness and how the brain works in general are boundless.

So, we don't discuss mental illness and we don't know much about it. This makes mental illness a less attractive discipline for would be health care professionals and the case for funding difficult to make in terms of measurable performance (both in terms of number of sufferers, or in terms of successful treatment).

We have already seen how unhelpful secrecy is in dealing with clinical depression. I will tell some stories that demonstrate to my satisfaction that the same applies to all mental health illness. After each story I give my view which I develop from story to story.

Those are my stories. They tell me that as a Society we know little about mental illness even though most of us will suffer some form of it sometime during our lives. Without a public debate, treatment is mysterious and specialists seem appropriately as different from other medical specialists as the mentally ill do compared to physical illness. Mental illness is the Cinderella branch of medicine, underfunded, underappreciated and underperforming.

In this book I am open and honest about my clinical depression. I am not ashamed of my mental illness, but I am scared it might recur. If anyone thinks the less of me because I am telling everyone I have been mentally ill, then I consider that they have a problem, not me. And their problem is themselves. We can cure Society I believe if we openly admit the scale of the problem and seek to deal with it like any branch of medicine.

I call upon you all to remedy this evil ignorance in our midst:

- Government should launch a large scale public education programme on mental illness
- Health care workers should be open and honest about the illness.
- Sufferers should be encouraged to see mental and physical illnesses in the same way and be encouraged to discuss.
- Everyone should grow up and face the reality of mental illness and stop burying their heads in the sand.

Case A: The Student and the Psychiatrist: My First Experience.

I was 24 years old in my first year as an academic. One of our students was in difficulty; reputedly having outbursts of shouting, tearing down posters in the Student Union, appearing to be threatening and possibly violent to those who encountered him. It was agreed amongst the faculty that the first academic he next met should try and encourage him to seek help in the University Health Centre. I was the next academic he met.

We chatted normally for a while until he suddenly asked if I came from Manchester. I told him, as he repeatedly probed around the question, that I was completely sure I did not come from Manchester. Apparently satisfied we reverted to normal conversation again. And then I was asked if I was a Catholic by religion. I am not, so again under persistent questioning I had no difficulty in assuring him that this was the case. Back to more relaxed normal conversation.

Did I want to know why he was questioning me about Manchester and Catholicism? I was polite and said yes. I was informed as straight facedly as any other part of our conversation that the Catholics of Manchester were plotting to overthrow the Queen and replace her with the Pope. I asked the student if he had been feeling well lately, and he admitted that he had not but was not sure what the problem was. I suggested that he should seek expert advice, which I could arrange for him immediately.

He agreed and I phoned the Health Centre and with everyone's agreement I escorted my student there. A psychiatrist met us and invited me into the consultation room with them. A chance to see an expert in action, so in I went!

It was a repeat of the kind of conversation I had in my room with my student for 40 minutes, except this meeting was much shorter and rapidly heated up. On being questioned about Manchester or his Catholicism, the psychiatrist refused to answer the questions, telling my student to mind his own business and to stop being personal. The student responded with increasing anger at the lack of response and persisted ever less delicately with his questions. The psychiatrist met him head on; eventually the student was so enraged he stormed out of the room. The psychiatrist, red faced with anger, informed me that my student was "a psychotic, schizophrenic ..." or some such listing of many mental health terms. I was not impressed.

The student was found by the police on a public highway after they had been called by someone who felt threatened by him, and he agreed voluntarily to go into a mental hospital for treatment. He rejoined the course some months later and finished the course successfully.

This story took place about 35 years ago, so it could be said that things have improved since then. It was my first time at having to deal directly with someone who was mentally ill, and I thought I did quite well, especially when I managed to persuade the sufferer to seek help which I personally ensured he would have by escorting him to the expert. Clearly my expectations were too high. And yet, I had no experience of such things before, so I had no way of assessing what I could or should have expected.

Case B: Quality of Life

As a young man with children, I was now more mature. One of the friends of the family, recently retired, was taken into hospital with a prostate problem and operated on. He was informed that the operation was a total success and that if he took some medication he would be well. He took the medicine but did not feel well, and became progressively depressed as his health diagnosis was always good, even though he felt increasingly unwell. The pressure became too much and he publicly declared his wish to die in fairly dramatic outbursts, although never a danger to anyone. On the advice of his doctor, I took him to a mental hospital accompanied by one of his daughters. Since I was not a blood relative, the psychiatrist we met at the hospital insisted that he talk with the daughter on their own. They came back to me, the daughter in tears, and the psychiatrist informed me that they had both agreed that we should take the man home.

I then asked what seemed to me to be a very reasonable question – would the psychiatrist please tell us how to look after the man? I must admit the answer was a complete surprise to me. The psychiatrist immediately said he would admit the man, and that was done there and then.

There were things that happened during the man's stay that I shall always feel guilty about. Several times for instance he looked as though he had been in a 'fight' but apparently he had 'fallen down some stairs'! What should I do? I had no idea what happened when we were not there. If I complained, would that help or would he fall down stairs even more often? If this seems obvious to you, then see if the finale of the hospital part of this story influences your view.

Leading up to the man's hospital release, a case conference of his care workers and relatives was called. The psychiatrist chairing the meeting asked what the family wanted to do. First to reply, I asked what the options were. The chair asked me if I was a blood relative and informed me to keep quiet since I was not!

Never himself again, the man went home, deteriorated, was taken into hospital and died. By now I wanted to know the truth and asked the prostate surgeon if the man had been suffering from cancer all along. Yes. Why was he told he was OK? It was felt he would have more difficulty with knowing that he had cancer than not. And why, the surgeon added, was I complaining, he had lived almost two years since surgery! What about quality of life I asked? I got no answer. I was not impressed with this incident either.

This story took place about 25 to 30 years ago, so it could be claimed to be irrelevant today. What I observe nevertheless is the lack of openness with the patient which led to him living in a world of slowing increasing doubt, discomfort, fear and finally terror. Even when being treated for depression, he was never told that he was physically ill. So the man took hormone medicine that developed his breasts, gave him hot flushes and of course did not suppress his cancer, merely slowed it down. And everyone told him there was nothing wrong with him. No wonder he became mentally ill. Secrecy, lack of honesty, and general ignorance amongst the non-professionals did him great harm. My ignorance when I look back is scarcely believable to me.

Case C: The Mental Illness Merry-Go-Round

Much later in my career, as Dean of a Faculty, I was informed that one of our students was acting in an intimidating and offensive manner to the female staff in the University. I was also told that he had a history of mental illness. I met with the student who was quite agitated and I listened to his claim of abuse. Maybe abuse of some sort was being perpetrated, but by whom and to whom I had no way of knowing. At that time he was fairly coherent, but he deteriorated so that female colleagues felt in danger in his presence. In a very bad state he turned up at my office, causing consternation. I thought he clearly needed help, and since no one had succeeded so far, I took it upon myself.

I escorted the student to the Health Centre, waited patiently, and discussed his case with a doctor, who recommended he go to a specialist mental illness which was attached to one of the local hospitals. I drove the student there, and we waited a while more – aware of my being a University Professor meant we waited less than otherwise I guess..

The specialist unit was having nothing to do with this case; they did not have the facilities to handle dangerous patients. I patiently asked what help could we get the student and I was recommended to go to a very specialist secure unit nearby. More travel, more waiting, everyone being very civilised to me. But then a specialist questioned the student, doubted much of what he said and ended by asking what medication the student was on. None.

Irritated we were informed that the starting point in the system was treatment with the patient's doctor, and only if reasonable attempts had been made and failed could the student then qualify to be referred to this unit.

In spite of my attempts to make sense out of the situation, it was clear that nothing was going to change the position.

So back we both went to the University Health Centre and waited. I explained what had happened since we had left the Centre in the morning. Without comment the doctor prescribed for my student, and I was informed that since the student was now much calmer than he been when we made our morning visit, I should leave the student to find his way home and try his medication. The student was several weeks later admitted for specialist care and the last I heard he was improving. Looking back on the day, I was not impressed.

This case occurred less than 8 years ago. I was not informed correctly about any aspect of what was going on at any time of the day. I found the student responded gradually to my attention, but all the experts either gave him cursory recognition or were just hostile. I have never experienced anything like this in any other branch of medicine in my life. I believe that this treatment occurs because nobody wants to discuss mental illness, so there are few controls on what goes on.

Case D: This Student Needs Telling Off: Ignorance About Mental Illness

I came across a disturbance in the Department's administrative offices. One of our students was swearing loudly at almost everyone in sight and many people were upset. I asked what was going on, and I was told that the student had a history of mental illness and had apparently gone mad again.

A professorial colleague marched off to his office and then a few minutes later the student emerged from the administrative offices, face aglow and we exchanged a few pleasantries. As he left I was told he was being taken to the Professor's office to be "told off" for his behaviour. I was astonished and explained this was not a very good idea. If he was mad, being "told off" would have no normal meaning for him. And if the student was confronted aggressively I had no idea if he would react violently, not knowing what form of madness he had. As the force of what I was saying struck home, someone moved off quickly to the Professor's office to head off the "telling off".

The student later was admitted for treatment. Then the question of his status and registration arose, especially with regard to his funding and registration period. I was consulted on possible courses of action. I pointed out that although I appreciated the logic and rationality of the proposals they were all a waste of time since the student was not in a fit mental state to appreciate logic or rationality or anything else. Nothing could be discussed and decided until the student was well again.

The student did become well enough to resume studies.

I was very unimpressed by the lack of understanding that I and my colleagues displayed concerning a student going mad for a while.

This story is from only 6 years ago. It demonstrates that the average person has no idea about what mental illness is. Such illness is not discussed, merely reacted to. Consequently the chances of someone who becomes mentally ill getting appropriate handling by a non specialist is very low and more luck if correct than good judgement.

Physical health has flourished through advances in medicine, public health awareness, better diets, better exercise regimes and an army of specialist agencies to treat and pamper all and any physical parts of or bodies. If we achieve the above four objectives, I believe that similar benefits for mental illness are also obtainable.

For everyone's sake, please join me in achieving this. Whenever the opportunity arises, face the challenge and force discussion, do not let any mention of mental illness be discretely ignored and put in the trash bin called "secret: do not discuss."

CHAPTER 3

MY PHYSICAL MOVEMENT

This chapter and the next look at the more intimate things in my life: dressing and washing at one level; moving around in crowded areas; how Society helps me with my difficulties with movement; impacts on my mental well being; and the direct effects on people to people interaction. This chapter starts with a broad look at these matters and provides an appropriate detailed coverage of my physical movement: The aspects of physical movement looked at are: movement in everyday life, starting at the personal level; movement in combination with other people; and then broader movement issues, covering the support that comes from various organisations in Society ranging from financial support to physical aids.

I conclude the chapter with my overall views on how I cope with my movement problems as a Parkinson's sufferer. It is worth remembering that this chapter and the next, like chapter two on clinical depression, are not meant to be describing the fate of every Parkinson's sufferer, but what is happening to me. Some parts will be in common with many other Parkinson's sufferers, and some will be less common if not entirely unique.

3.1 SEX, DRUGS AND ROCK MY SOUL

This and the next chapter concern the immediate impacts on me as the individual Ray Paul. They are matters that affect me personally and in some cases possibly uniquely as I roll along in life with Parkinson's disease. So this section starts with a general overview, then discusses the medical regime I live with, before moving on to coverage of 'ordinary' depression (not the clinical depression covered in the previous chapter). In other words, I start the chapter with this section on approaches to handling Parkinson's disease. Then there follows two sections on the direct physical effects, first when I am on my own, and secondly when I am interacting with other people. The broadening out of the issues related to my physical movement continues with sections on: support given by the State to help with movement problems; followed by a section on recognition as a disabled driver and how this is a great help to me; and then a section on how I am monitored to ensure my driving is not only safe for me, but also for everyone else. Lastly I conclude the chapter by giving my overall view on how well I think I am doing physically living with Parkinson's disease. Because dancing is such an important part of my life, I have separated out dancing's major impacts and benefits into the last chapter, although of course it is mentioned many times during this chapter.

So let us start with 'dealing with life' approaches to having the disease. I think there are three possible levels at which a sufferer can react to having such an illness. Three in the sense that they are a description of 'model' cases that can be useful for dialog even though they might not fit any one sufferer exactly. But I suspect all sufferers fit somewhere in between the three models, and probably use different mixtures of these levels for different aspects of their lives. The three possible levels are:

- To give up and wait like a vegetable to pass on
- To fit one's life around the illness, to restrict one's self to what the illness will now allow you to do.
- To determine that the illness will not be allowed to affect your life if it can be avoided, even though the cost incurred may appear excessive to others.

Now at this point I wish to make it clear that in my personal opinion there is no evidence that convinces me that the 'level' any particular sufferer operates at is entirely their choice. Parkinson's disease is a variety of illnesses of the same family, and this may affect one's approach to the 'choice' of level. Similarly treatments can be very individual, and their effects do not have to be the same from sufferer to sufferer. And lastly, the external environment as always will be a major factor. So my view is that the way a sufferer rolls with life or not is not open to judgement by non-sufferers no matter how convenient it would be if the reactions were different. Of course the third approach might be considered more convenient for friends and family but the first approach may be all the sufferer can do. I have come to recognise through this type of reflection that my approach, whilst not consciously deliberate as far as I am aware, was probably a natural extension of the way I had developed in handling life (especially after my 'conversion' to ambition, after a decade of my career had slipped away).

I am level three with a vengeance, as this book amply illustrates. I tell people I really do not like being ill, and they retort often with exasperation that nobody does. But what I mean is that I will seek any way of handling myself that will minimise the impact on my life.

I take a lot of drugs (about 30 a day at the time of writing). Many of them are performance enhancing, co-enzymes, dopamine substitutes and direct replacements, all inducing greater physical performance. So successful are these performance enhancing drugs that, when there has been no other medical condition to restrict my activities on top of my Parkinson's disease, I have stayed up all night about once a month, quite simply (as is discussed below) because I easily wander from activity to activity. Time seems to drift by, and everyone else is asleep and so no one interrupts me, and then dawn breaks. Under these circumstances I can function at a reduced level for that day, but it is in general not good for me (especially mentally – as will be explained in the next chapter).

Obviously the performance enhancing drugs affect my libido too, fortunately positively. I could at this point discuss my sexual activity, but the only difference Parkinson's disease makes is the need not to stay in the same position for too long, and an increase in variable skin sensitivity. The latter variability can raise the need for physical contact to almost desperate levels for short periods of time. Otherwise the subject is not worth discussing, but for the inquisitive I make the following observations about anyone else's sexual behaviour and activities: What goes on between two or more consenting adults of a sexual nature is their business and no one else's. Each should hold the confidences of the other(s) in such matters. Therefore, so shall I.

Physically the effect of Parkinson's disease or the drugs is hard to explain. In the early years of treatment, it sometimes felt as though there was a drugs war going on inside my body, and the effect was to completely flatten me. I just sat looking stunned until the medicine had sorted itself out. I now have some start up medication for when I wake up which has almost stopped this happening (the effect was usually at breakfast when the major intake of drugs takes place for the day). Even so, I often feel disembodied especially in the morning, a bit like being jet-lagged where the brain and body seem to float apart. This can be an increasingly pleasant sensation in a 'floating' sort of way, but not when it leads to the control of bodily functions appearing to be remote. This lack of control over one's movements can in itself be a bit depressing. Feeling low then militates against the obvious solution to the problem, which is almost any form of physical activity (the gym, making love) or sensation (cold showers?!?!) that accentuates the sensations received by the body to the brain. Dancing is an obvious outlet for me, as previously discussed and to be discussed further later in the last chapter.

On other occasions the medicine seems to be too much and I go into hyper-movement mode, not being able to stop twitching or swaying. Sitting down or doing something slow and detailed will not happen. Again, since I like dancing, I use this as a 'cure' – but I guess in this case to wear me out enough for the excess energy behind the hyper-movement to be dissipated.

Too much physical activity can drain the strength of the body and then one has moved from depressive disconnectivity or excessive connectivity to tired lethargy which can also be depressive. Constant attention to these potential extremes pays off in terms of a balanced lifestyle. Lack of attention contributes to tardiness or absence. If I am unable to move properly, either too fast or too slow, it becomes very difficult to focus activity sufficiently to bring all the necessary clothing and materials together and be washed and dressed to be on time for the first appointment of the day. Those who know me try to avoid being given the first appointment since this is often the longest wait of all the day's appointments, especially if I decide not to go to work at all.

The best way to describe how I handle the depressive moods is through the advice I give to others in a similar situation. As discussed in Chapter 2, be not idle, for that gives the imagination time to work on the negative aspects and reinforce them. No matter how bad you feel, even to the point of not loving yourself too much, remember there are many people in your life who love you. They deserve your well-being, since a disregard for that can be devastating for them – in other words very selfish of you! Depressive moods are not the fault of the sufferer and a large minority of the population (about a third apparently) will be in your position at some time or other. So you are not abnormal or unusual, quite the opposite. As an aside Jasna found an article in a newspaper that reported that taking zinc seemed to reduce depression in mentally ill patients. I take zinc daily, and the benefits are that if I move into a depressive mood, it rarely is one of the freefall crashes I used to have. Apart from such crashes being an extremely unpleasant sensation, it is very hard to stop them and to climb back up from them. Zinc suppressed mood swings can be arrested more readily although they are perhaps more frequent.

Three years ago I slowly switched pergolide tablets with increasingly larger rotigotine transdermal patches, and the mood swings became increasingly infrequent – maybe I was too busy scratching my skin reactions to the patches to notice! But I have moved on from patches and the depression rate is still lower than it was. Maybe Pergolide was the cause of my clinical depression? But still, even though quite rare now, about two or three times a year, for no apparent reason, I go into freefall (a very unpleasant sensation) and end up very low for at least the rest of the day.

But largely my medication is very successful. Obviously my medication has followed the regimes outlined by my consultant in his Invited Contribution which follows the chapters in this book.

3.2 PHYSICALLY, THE PERSONAL LEVEL

I have already explained in section 1.6 that I need time, space and speed for Parkinson's disease's physical effects to be overridden or manageable. If not, the impacts are varied but they all more or less make things slower, more difficult or impossible depending to some extent on the efficacy of my medication at the time.

Getting dressed and undressed is an obvious difficulty at times. If I am slightly off and no help is available, putting on a shirt can take up to 20 minutes because of the buttons. Half buttoning the shirts when laundering them can help, although getting a shirt stuck half-way over my head and shoulders and finding a button too many done up can lead to some interesting physical decision making: whether in that state to try and undo the button, as if undoing buttons 'on the ground' was not difficult enough; or trying to remove the shirt (not always straight forward) and then undoing and trying again. Whichever method is used, finding the shirt arm holes can be more difficult for me than playing golf is for some people.

Putting underpants, trousers and socks and shoes on – should this be done sitting down (and then trying to lift enough to get the first two over the lower regions, followed by trying to stand up) or by trying to balance as you go (which provides for interesting decisions concerning pulling out of a move or risk falling over)? I often wear a suit when going into a working environment and when asked why I don't dress more easily and casually, I find myself explaining my belief that people think there is a relationship between the way you look and your ability. I also feel good if I dress well, and of course I do not like the idea of 'giving in'. These can be seen as noble attributes if one wants to, but there is a cost. For example, several times I have been to meetings wearing a long sleeved shirt with button-free cuffs and then put the cufflinks on during the meeting – sometimes over a minimum 30 minute period. People kindly offer to help, but I assure them I must face the challenge. One good friend said afterwards he would have helped but he guessed I wanted to win myself and he knew I would ask otherwise.

I have at any time a variety of bruises on my body. When the medication is not quite kicking in, or it is towards the end of a very long day, or I have been physically overdoing it, there is a balancing problem to watch out for, as well as the normal movement defects associated with Parkinson's disease, which are lurching, stumbling and cogwheeling. For the first six or seven years I rarely went completely over, but the need to seek some nearby support can be bought at a medium impact of the body on the support object. And it is as well to be aware of physical limitations even when the medication is working. Lately I guess I am falling down about once a month, which I am fairly used to so I tend to land without much damage.

Problems with physical movement change over time, so just when you think you are on top of the problem a new variation pops up. For example even with medication, the decision to start to walk can end up being translated at the action level as a series of short stumbling steps, or no response from the legs at all. Being aware of the effects means one can help anticipate them and take action (usually stopping). Recently I have experienced start up situations where I concentrate on starting and everything says A OK and off we go – except that the legs are lying, they have sent a message/sensation saying they are moving but they are not. The first few weeks I experienced this phenomenon I found I was on the floor before I was aware there was a problem. Extra awareness is quickly learnt!

Have you observed how you sit down? Let me tell you – you descend onto the selected target and then you make small adjustments until you feel comfortable. These adjustments are so natural and slight to imperceptible that you may not notice them. But Parkinson's sufferers know all about them because they do not make the adjustments. They are too slight and slow to be carried out unless the sufferer is sitting down whilst concentrating solely on doing that. But you cannot spend your life paying close attention to every movement that you make; else you would have no existence other than movement thinking. So the sufferer sits and stays where they land. Since the reason people make the small adjustments is because otherwise the seated position would soon become uncomfortable, it follows that a Parkinson's sufferer is soon feeling uncomfortable. And then there is getting up from any seated or prone position. It just is not fun.

There are similar difficulties that go with sleeping in bed. Quite often before I would like to get up, I am awoken in the early hours of the morning by which time the body has accumulated a range of aches and pains for not lying properly when going to bed and then not making fine natural adjustments during sleep. The chances of going back to sleep with such physical irritations are sometimes so small that often the only thing to do is get up. I do sometimes go back to bed for a nap later but 'get-you-going' medication can make it seem that this is unnecessary. If I am not careful, then accumulated sleep deprivation could be a problem.

Just as difficult can be on those occasions when one is awoken by the need to go to the toilet. When this happens, obviously the medication is at a low intensity, so control of fine bodily functions is at its most difficult. The need to go is intense. But getting out of the bed can be breathtakingly time consuming (up to 15 minutes). The covers and sheets are best removed otherwise the covered parts of the anatomy are difficult to move. Rolling can speed up the process, if there is space enough to do this. If Jasna is there and is awoken by my desperate infrequent movements, she will kindly propel me to a takeoff position with her feet – yes, she kicks me out of bed! If my immobility is severe she will get up and help me out. Emergency measures should always be to hand to avoid accidents.

If I have problems moving before going to bed, I often used to try and dance through the immobility. If this proved difficult, I saw this as a challenge and kept going. The net result can be worse than just going to bed, but I do not like being physically defeated. The semi-recumbent bike can also be used to kick start normal physical activity as well as improving leg muscles to deal with red leg syndrome (discussed in greater detail in a later chapter). The sad fact is I should use the bike more often for both reasons but I prefer dancing because when successful it can be exhilarating.

In general if I stay in one position for too long (say more than an hour) I start to 'seize' up. So when I am working, like typing in this book to the computer, I have to remember to break off periodically and move around. This is one of the reasons why I often read PhDs writings whilst dancing. The student usually takes up less than an hour of my time, but may be one of many appointments in sequence so I must take a movement or dancing opportunity whenever I can.

You have heard the expression 'Water, water everywhere and not a drop to drink'. If I have a glass of water I may raise it to my lips several times, but ending up drinking none. If I do not think about it, that final adjustment that gently tips the glass just as drinking starts does not occur. More realistically, a glass of wine can last all evening since I never drink any even though the glass has passed my lips many times. This could be seen as good alcohol intake control, but not drinking enough liquid, especially water, also leads to poor to abysmal body movement and control. Cramp and other manifestations of this can be dealt with by a conscious and rapid intake of ½ to a litre of water. My method of dealing with this problem when it is recurring too often is to use a sports water bottle to drink from, which requires the bottle to be tipped upside down first before delicate drinking control movements. This ensures some attention is paid to drinking otherwise one is wearing the liquid and not drinking it. But wine in a sports bottle!!

At all times my posture can be undermining me, as it is easy to adopt a slumped posture which does nothing for balance, and I can start tipping over slowly if I do not check occasionally. A slumped posture includes bent knees, something like a wicketkeeper in cricket or a catcher in baseball, although not with spread knees. It is surprisingly difficult to make any kind of useful movement with bent knees, including dancing. I have lately taken to energy drinks and energy pills which appear to help me considerably. I take these daily, either when I have gone 'off' between scheduled pill takings, or because I can feel the pills starting to become less effective.

When I am out in the street walking with Jasna she tells me that from behind it looks to her as though I am fiddling with my shoulders as I walk. This may be the effect of walking quickly which often leaves her following me from behind, giving her ample study time for understanding and/or commenting on any aspect of my walking movement. Incidentally leather soled shoes are, all other things being equal, by far the best for 'feeling' the ground and therefore balancing and moving better. I have a variety of comfortable well-fitting leather-soled shoes/boots for all seasons and occasions. There is a problem with smooth, wet or frozen surfaces since leather-soled shoes will tend to slip unless great care is taken, but then Parkinson's sufferers spend their lives walking carefully.

And whilst giving advice, the new battery powered wet multi-razors seem ideal to me for gentleman's face shaving since the moving blades can make up for lack of good hand control. I also have several electric razors since I have discovered that different types of such razors will cut well to badly different parts of the face to each other. So using two electric razors one after the other gives reasonable shaves.

Jasna says when I can't move I keep closing my eyes and licking my lips like a big lizard, which whilst not flattering, provides some information as to my health status. I can be extremely slow in movement, but with a hotel's or host's awareness of my state of health it can be very easy to get help.

Sometimes when I am 'off' my facial expression can look from some angles like a half-demented village idiot especially when its owner is tired. Everyone is extremely polite and courteous to me still which is helpful. But how can you assure people when you do not quite look well or with-it?

The five senses are our prime methods of finding out about our external surroundings. Mine are affected in the following ways:

See. When I am tired I have at times had some spectacular hallucinations as will be discussed in the next chapter.

Hear. I have always been softly spoken, but now I find it very difficult to know how to pitch my voice since at apparently quite low volumes it registers as fine going out to me. When I am tired I can also hear 'sounds' (again I shall discuss these in the next chapter).

Taste. My sense of taste is reduced in range and intensity.

Smell. I have a lowered sense of smell, and some things I can no longer smell at all (mushrooms for example – nor can I taste them). Half or more of the plants in the garden also have no smell for me, even though strong to other people. Cigarette smokers do not bother me unless condemned to a Ghetto room in the building and I accidentally go into the room too.

Touch. I still have high sensitivity through touch and this works both ways in the sense that I can still 'feel' another person's mood quite well and feel a mood swing, as well as being very aware of my own body or not.

So looking after oneself is no easy task, and at times can be impossible. When the medicine is not working (if I forgot to take it, or I have just woken up) and I am 'off', then everything is either monumentally slow or cannot be done. And that is just one person making for complications. But when you add other people into the scenario, it can become even worse as will be seen in the next section, although the potential is for improvement.

3.3 PHYSICALLY, INTERACTIONS WITH OTHER PEOPLE

Public places are potentially difficult places for me in that if there are too many people in close proximity to me I cannot move. If this state lasts too long, a panic or anxiety attack can be triggered. For example I attended the degree awarding ceremony at Brunel University in 2007, being placed where I could slip in and out so that I did not seize up by being in the same position for too long. Afterwards I waited to congratulate my tutees personally and for pictures to be taken of us together in our academic gowns. This was still within the building itself and after a while I realised that the number of people building up was going to make life difficult for me. Armed with my secretary Carole and a student we tried to get out as soon as possible but the exits were few and narrow and people were in no hurry, so it must have taken 15 minutes or so to get out. Panic started to grip me so when I emerged I was into a mild anxiety attack which took 30 to 60 minutes to suppress. Dancing was helpful, but I also needed time and space completely to myself, which fortunately Carole ensured for me.

To avoid crowds I tend to drive my car whenever I can or take taxis. For long distances I use air travel since this tends to provide easier access and exit space than railway stations. Even so, a few years ago I went to Heathrow Airport to fly to Zagreb to join Jasna for a long weekend (she had gone several days ahead). When I got to the terminal, British Airways computer systems were down and it was chaos. There were people queuing with their bags not knowing what the queue was for, there were people moving around with their bags not knowing where they were going, and the British Airways staff could not help since all their information was computer based. Reasoning hard, I managed to check in electronically but I had a check-in bag and the fast bag drop was not operating. And then I saw 'awkward shaped bags check in' which operated for all airlines and nearly persuaded them to let my bag in – until we realised that if it was not checked in and labelled properly it would not go anywhere, and this check in was for awkward luggage already checked in. After an hour and a half of this the anxiety level was too high for me to stay in the midst of this chaos so I went to the British Airways ticket desk and said I wanted a ticket refund. Airlines are never keen to do this, but to the credit of the ticket personnel, she took one look at my face and immediately refunded the ticket, whereupon I returned home.

I never travel light; I always take too many things 'just in case'. This can cause me problems with baggage allowances, but I have to admit the airlines tend to be very good when I explain I carry extra stuff because I have Parkinson's disease. With only one exception I have not been charged excess baggage.

When I am out and about and people see me not balancing as well as normal, they often and for the right motivation try to help me. Unfortunately this can be more damaging than helpful since my problems with balance I need to address myself. If a third party takes hold of me, that immediately reduces the control I over my ability to balance, hence making the balancing problem even worse. Jasna has tried several times to support me by my arm and move me forward, but as soon as someone does that, I immediately go into 'freeze' mode and could if the pressure is maintained just keel over. For example, see the How Not to Move Vignette.

Being restricted in movement by the proximity of other people also means that the simple pleasure of walking hand-in-hand is not possible unless the other person can completely anticipate my speed and direction of movement. Similarly for trivial activities such as getting in and out of cars, helping me can be quite a hindrance.

Then there are simple things which I need help with that I have stopped being as embarrassed about as I used to be. For example, if I am served a meal with some meat or sea food that needs careful or forceful cutting, Jasna usually calmly takes my plate and cuts or prepares the problem items. I have on occasion asked someone else to do this for me rather than struggle unsuccessfully, inelegantly and frustratingly myself.

How Not to Move Vignette

In March 2009 I accompanied Jasna on a skiing holiday to Val d'Isere, but found the air too thin for my weakened heart, which had not mended enough at that time. I ended up being taken down the mountain to a small hospital for some tests and at 4am I was taken from the treatment room to a two-person ward. It would have taken too much time to change the beds over in the room, so the quickest thing to do would be to transfer me. At 4am I am not at my best, so as I got out of the bed and tried with difficulty to balance, the nurse decided to help me. Communication was at a basic level (none), so without warning the nurse took hold of me to support me across the ten metres gap between the beds. The effect was that I immediately lost my balance and the whole of my weight was transferred to the nurse to hold on to. She told me repeatedly in French not to put all my weight on her, and I told her repeatedly to let go so I could balance. We lurched across the room to the accompaniment of "Non, non!" from the nurse mixed in with my request in English "to let go." We both arrived at the bed exhausted.

I came round to accepting this state of affairs after I attended a lunch party at a friend's house where I tried to do it alone, struggled impotently with a well-cooked piece of duck which however still required decisive cutting, and looked at the end of the meal as if I had not appreciated the food at all. I felt the need to explain to the hostess afterwards, which made my keeping the problem to myself during the meal quite perverse!

Of course there have been occasions when I have gone 'off' and I have been helped by considerate people in a very constructive way. For example the Going Nowhere Fast Vignette tells of my rescue from a state almost of being marooned.

Lastly, why are so many medications for Parkinson's sufferers packaged in such a way as to make it almost impossible for the sufferer to get them out of the packaging unaided – unbelievable!

Going Nowhere Fast Vignette

We were on holiday in 2008, taking our annual break at the Hotel Croatia in Cavtat. This was at the time I was probably at my lowest because of anaemia and all the other problems that were related to some negative side effects of previous medicine. I was in the coffee shop area of the hotel foyer, close to some tourist shops. I had been working on this book at one of the tables when I decided to go back to my room. As I packed my things up, I realised I was going 'off'. I did not have my telephone with me, so I could not call Jasna. So with increasing difficulty I got ready and moved away from the table. In the middle of no man's land between the shop and the coffee shop seating area my attempt to go to my room ground to a complete halt.

I tried all my movement tricks – walking backwards, trying to pirouette into forward movement – nothing worked. I stayed stuck for about 30 minutes, and although if there had been an observer I should have looked sufficiently unusual to be worth an inquiry, no one came near me. In fact, if anything, because of my seemingly frozen position, people were more likely to go around me than be inquisitive. I was getting fairly uptight which of course did not help. At last Car, the lady running the newsagents/general shop, saw me and rushed out of her shop to help. This was picked up on by Dunja, the lady running the jewellery shop next to Car, who also rushed across to see if she could help. Car has someone in her family with Parkinson's disease and was fairly familiar with my predicament.

The ladies got me moving under my advice by slowly pulling me by the arms into movement at a speed that then became self-sustaining. Since Dunja's shop was the easiest to leave unattended (under the watchful eye of other shop keepers), it was Dunja who escorted me all the way back to my room. It seemed trivial to her, a ten minute act of kindness, but it brought to an end an increasingly anxiety generating state which I did not know how I was going to get out of or when. I now try and carry a telephone at all times. Thank you Car and Dunja.

3.4 STATE BENEFITS: DISABILITY AND MOBILITY

Having looked at personal considerations to do with movement, and then at interactions with other people, I am now going to go another level higher and look at the general help I get from Society with my movement problems. Some of these are financial, as in this section, and some are a mixture of financial and facilitating, especially mobility. Although my experiences with State support are obviously UK based, I have no doubt that the lessons I can draw are universally applicable.

I have to admit, I was reluctant to seek State aid for reasons I am not fully sure of myself. I did not apply for any form of benefit for seven years, possibly for any one or more of the following reasons:

- Maybe this is a form of denial about my illness
- I did not relish the intricacies of filling in the application forms
- I did not need the money (at first)
- I did not want to be officially labelled 'disabled'.

Jasna did fill in some forms for me earlier on, but I did not send them in.

I occasionally in the years following retirement in 2003, looked up web pages on state benefits that I might be entitled to, but my need had not been sufficient to encourage me to make sense of the plethora of information, the ins and outs of job seekers who are disabled, people who cannot seek jobs because they are too disabled, special provisions if you are young, special provisions if you are old, whether a benefit is means tested or not, and whether in order to claim benefit B you must claim benefit A first (even though you may get nothing for A, an entitlement to A may be required to apply for B). Those people who enjoyed the film *Life of Brian* by the Monty Python's Flying Circus members will possibly also enjoy some of the film's re-enactment in this part of my story.

In 2007 I decided to make an attempt to find my way through this jungle. I was motivated by loss of income (the Income Protection Plan to be described in 6.3 ceased when I was 60 in July 2007) and also by the desire to make travel easier by being able to use disabled car parking facilities. The latter is more easily acquired if you already are a claimant in the welfare system (I found this to be largely true).

As far as I can tell, I have to claim incapacity benefit in order to claim disability living allowance, which I have to claim in order to claim motability allowance. The last of these would undoubtedly make car driving much more economical for me, and as I shall explain in section 3.6 below, car driving is very important to me.

But I am running ahead of myself. First, incapacity benefit. I filled in an online form on the web and sent it in. There was enormous redundancy on the form since it had a widespread usage (was I currently a resident of one of Her Majesty's prisons...?). After some exchange of communications I was telephone interviewed by a very pleasant competent lady. Much more extensive, much more redundancy. She apologised several times, but it was not her fault. At the end she said she would send a printout in the post for me to check and for documentary evidence etc.

Whilst awaiting developments I received a letter from National Insurance (essentially a tax on income for national health and pension provision) informing me I had not fully paid up for the tax financial year 2005-06. The letter explained that I was short by 52 weeks and I could pay up if I wanted to. Why would I want to do that? Well, apparently a full state pension required 30 years of payments. I had so far accumulated 36 years so would I like to pay? I was tempted to ask for a 6 year refund, but it would not amuse the person opening the letter.

My incapacity benefit claim went in and just before Christmas I received a barrage of communications:

- You are entitled to incapacity benefit
- You must send a sick note from your doctor for September
- You are entitled to £0 because your income is too high
- You must send a sick note from your doctor covering the next few weeks or your benefit might not be paid.
- Get us a sick note before Christmas or you will receive no benefit

My head was reeling; doctors are not widely available around Christmas; a zero benefit being cut did not seem too serious; so I went away for 10 days. When I came back, more post, with much more desirable messages:

- I am recognised officially as incapacitated
- I do not need any doctors sick notes
- Do not send any sick notes
- I will continue to receive £0 benefit
- My National Insurance for 2005-06 is fully paid up since I was incapacitated

I drew breath and then in September 2008 I sought disability living allowance (DLA) which is not means tested and which has several levels for two categories, care and mobility. I needed the top level in both categories to get maximum benefit from the motability scheme. I shall now try and explain these labels:

- DLA in general is paid to a disabled person depending on their level of disability. The more help in general the claimant requires, the more money awarded. However, the money awarded can be spent exactly how the claimant wishes. This enables the claimant to make mature decisions about how to use the money to make their disability more tolerable, and there is no interference from officials who might otherwise claim to know better. It is a surprisingly imaginative and responsible way to provide assistance.
- There are two components
  - Care, largely to meet the ordinary needs of the disability

- o Mobility, to enable the claimant to move around in the outside world
- Motability is a special scheme that can basically give the claimant a new vehicle every three years fully taxed, insured and maintained. This provision would be in exchange for the mobility part of the DLA if the latter is awarded at the top rate.

The application form for a DLA is ferociously comprehensive, going in to great detail about distances one can move unaided in different circumstances, frequency of help required, the domestic situation, limitations on ability to conduct a full life etc. I filled in the forms interactively on the web until the system crashed irrevocably. I salvaged the forms I had managed to complete, finished the rest by printing onto blank forms or even hand wrote some. I sent the whole collection off with a covering note explaining the circumstances. I half expected to get the whole lot back and told to do it again. I was pleasantly surprised. I was awarded a DLA with both categories at the top level!

If I were to give advice on filling in such applications, it would be to take the worst case scenarios as the case for the award. With a disability like Parkinson's disease, one's state of health can fluctuate a lot and often. It only makes sense to be given support for the worst case scenarios, which could be at anytime and for any length of time. One cannot fill in forms every two or three weeks as circumstances change, there would be no end to form filling. The administrative burden would be overwhelming, and hugely expensive, so one is doing the best by everyone.

As an added bonus I discovered that incapacity benefit is not means tested if the DLA is awarded at the top level, although it is considered part of income for tax purposes.

So, at last after nearly 9 years I fought my way through the welfare benefits that I was entitled to. I have to say on reflection, the decision making process turned out to be quite straight forward. I am impressed by the DLA allowing the claimant to make his or her own responsible decisions as to how to spend the benefit in their own interests. I can only recommend that if you are disabled, put your claim in, it is likely to make life more tolerable one way or another

3.5 DISABLED CAR STICKER

In the U.K. local authorities (towns or districts) control the issue of disabled stickers to put in the car. Such a sticker can provide free or cheaper parking; more space for parking; a reduction in the normal parking restrictions; and special parking space in the road outside the disabled person's house. I have already indicated above that I was trying to fight my way through the benefits system to the point where the issue of such a sticker would be automatic, which indeed it was after I had achieved my DLA.

I could have just made an application and then I would have to be assessed. I did in fact go to the local authorities' offices to make such an application three or four years ago. I entered a large Victorian style room, in which there were a number of welfare claimants waiting or chatting. After a while an official appeared and asked fairly publicly and directly, who was I and what did I want?

Having rather publicly established the answers to these questions, I was asked if I was receiving benefit this-that-and-the-other. I was told that I could fill in a form if I wished, but then I would probably need to be assessed, and this assessor came round every so many weeks or other. That concluded my rather public examination into my state of affairs. I left the office wondering if I preferred struggling with myself and my body, as opposed to disentangling publicly what I might or might not be able to get help with.

But with the award of my DLA at the top level, all I needed to do was fill in a form, produce appropriate supporting documentation and then appear at the same offices as four years earlier. The permit was issued on the spot – well maybe an hour waiting followed by an hour of painstaking form filling and a barrage of questions from the operative behind the counter. And the benefits?

Free parking most places I go to, or subsidised fees, free access to London's famous congestion charging zone, nearer access to wherever I want to be, free parking in resident's parking areas, parking on restricted parts of some roads, reduced times between locations etc. When my medication is working well, I sometimes feel a little embarrassed at using a disabled badge holder's parking bay, as I walk from my car very effortlessly. However, I am never sure that the return to the car will be so effortless, and hence I need the reassurance of convenient location. But overall, there is little doubt that my disabled badge has made mobility much better.

3.6 DRIVING LICENCE, MOTOR INSURANCE AND RISK

Parkinson's sufferers vary in their symptoms, reactions to medications, speed of change and general abilities. The inability to move limbs or falling over or fainting is obviously not compatible with the safe driving of a motor vehicle. So in the U.K Parkinson's sufferers must notify the authorities when Parkinson's disease is first diagnosed. The authorities for the U.K. are known as the Drivers Vehicle Licensing Centre (DVLC). A set of forms have to be completed and investigations conducted into the state the illness and medication leaves the Parkinson's sufferer in. This investigation takes about six weeks. Clearly it must be thorough not only for the safety of the Parkinson's sufferer, but also for the safety of the general public.

My car is my greatest mobility aid to the living of my life as normal as possible. Given that if I am surrounded by people I cannot move, most forms of public transport are too difficult/dangerous/anxiety making for me to contemplate. Buses and trains in particular I rarely touch. Air travel if managed carefully is OK; otherwise I drive myself or take taxis. Taxis can be expensive, so my favoured mode of transport is to drive myself.

I also enjoy driving, and always have. I do not even mind the pressure of driving in heavy traffic in big cities, London in particular where I live. Driving a car makes me the equal of anyone else in terms of mobility. Road positioning, route planning and adaptation and local knowledge can make journey times quite reasonable even compared to public transport, and of course wherever I go and whatever I do when I get there, I know on completion I do not have to worry about transport connections, timing, arrangements and so on, my car is waiting for me at my service. Parkinson's disease does not appear to have much influence on my life in these circumstances. I have never had any difficulty driving the car. In fact I believe my medicine enhances my mental awareness, so I feel I am a better driver.

Given the importance of my car to me, you can imagine my trepidation when I had to apply for permission to continue driving. And when permission came it was for three years only. For the first time in over 30 years of driving I no longer held an indefinite licence to drive, but a licence for a mere three years. The application for renewal in 2003 took the six weeks the system claims it needs to process it.

But in 2006, the renewal forms went astray, and I only remembered when the renewal date was fast approaching. Parkinson's disease easily makes me anxious when my well being is at stake. I know rationally that I have no problem driving, and that my medical reports would show that. So I know rationally that the renewal is fairly certain. But what if it is not renewed? Given what I have said above, you can imagine that anxiety would feed quite greedily from the loss of this great source of freedom. And then, suddenly renewal looms, and there is not time to go through the six week cycle if continuity of licence is to be assured. Frantic telephone calls, faxes and so on were made.

Everyone answering the telephone was professional and helpful. If I returned this form today, I would be covered. The next day, yes we received the fax but no you are not covered until we process the form. And the forms we sent in the post need to be in the return post too before you can be covered. A few days later, all the forms are in the system but have not been brought together and that might take 3 more days. But my licence expires tomorrow! Well phone tomorrow and we will try and chase the paperwork. The next day, I do not have a licence to drive my car – an awful sensation. Fortunately, the day after, everything is OK, I have permission to drive and the licence appears shortly after. Not an experience I wish to repeat. In 2009 everything was processed on time and another three years of freedom lie ahead of me.

I am very wary of having an accident. I am aware that it can sound silly to say something like this, but the fact is an accident could have an even greater effect on me than most motorists. Now of course, no one wants an accident. But unless you drive dangerously, an accident does not affect your licence. But with three year renewal and any accidents being added to the medical evidence, how can I know what effect these will have? My car has been involved in an accident which I recount in the Stress Clinic Vignette.

The Stress Clinic Vignette

I had an appointment at a stress echocardiogram clinic because some results in the U.S.A. suggested that the side effects of one of my medications might be some damage to the heart. A stress echocardiogram is where you start with a normal echocardiogram as a benchmark, and then chemicals are used to raise the work rate of the heart and see how it performs under stress. Jasna's car was in for service so she drove me to the hospital in my car.

I crossed the hospital grounds to the entrance to the building when I heard a crash. I looked round – there was a bus in the side of my car and my wife was in the car! Although I went back quickly I was surprised to find Jasna and the bus driver still in their drivers' seats, I quickly established that there were no injuries to anyone. Jasna was crying because she had damaged my car, but I was immensely relieved everyone was OK. Cars can be repaired with money, people less so.

I let the clinic know I was sorting out the accident, called our local cab driver that we use, Mr Malik, who immediately responded and took Jasna and the car contents home for me (and picked me up later), whilst I swapped details with the shaken bus driver and arranged for my car to be scraped off the road. The bus won the duel of course, and drove off under its own steam.

I went back to the Stress Clinic where I had lost my slot, and although they tried to fit me in, no other patients defaulted on their appointments. And anyway, they said, I had probably had enough stress for one day!

I did the test a month or two later and I was found to be in great shape. But since I am open and honest, I cannot recommend this treatment although I survived it. I found it particularly difficult and I asked the operatives of the equipment if they had ever tried it. "Oh no", they said, "far too intrusive". True.

Fortunately I have a Protected No Claims Bonus on my car so the accident would not cost me more than the excess on the policy, or so I thought. But when the insurance renewal demand came in, the amount had gone up. I made telephone enquiries. My No Claims Discount was unchanged as promised. So why had the cost gone up so much (allowing for inflation). Because now you have made a claim, you are a higher risk so the premium goes up, but the discount is the same! I assume that sounds as ridiculous to the reader as it does to me.

3.7 AN OVERVIEW OF MY PHYSICAL WORLD

A large percentage of the time I can move around almost as well as most people. But I never know when I am about to go 'off', where and why? On bad days I can lose half of the day quite easily. If I have a cold or some other minor illness, I can lose two thirds to three quarters of the day. A reader of one of the earlier versions of this book commented that she did not realise how much the function of mobility was such a major problem for Parkinson's disease sufferers. This is I guess because when immobile the sufferers are not usually in the public eye, they are probably out of sight somewhere trying to get mobile.

Dancing, stumbling or falling over, or breaking into uncontrollable tiny running steps are a bit embarrassing in public. People around you are likely to think you are drunk or slightly mad. Humans rush to judgement when they see the unusual instead of being curious and understanding the situation. I cannot blame anyone for doing this, it seems to be an overwhelming automatic reaction, driven by fear whenever we face the unknown. I hope the publication of this book will make a contribution to the reduction of fear as the unknown is explained more. Certainly in many personal encounters with members of the public, as soon as I explain the reasons for my dancing, or the causes of my tripping and unusual efforts to stay upright, I get a lot of support from these newly enlightened individuals.

CHAPTER 4

MY MENTAL STATE

In this chapter I describe the variety of ways my mental state has been affected by Parkinson's disease, and how these changes have had an impact on other peoples' mental states. This is a wide-ranging chapter which attempts to give the reader an insight into the changed world that someone who is diagnosed with Parkinson's disease can expect to enter. The first two sections introduce the probably unexpected change whereby the sufferer finds that if they want to engage in activity, it can often only be achieved by faster actions and reactions. The third and fourth sections deal with those aspects of the mind whereby the brain either is underperforming or over performing (section three for the former, section four for the latter). Some of these effects are also discussed as part of the 'great escape' section (section 5), where the author is let loose to help a variety of people, resulting in a multiplicity of effects for the people concerned.

The sixth section attempts to give my wife Jasna's point of view, with some responses by me. The things that affect me mentally in sections 1 to 4 have a direct impact on my ultimate carer/partner/love of my life, Jasna. I explain in this penultimate section of the chapter why it is that the spouse is probably about as much affected by such an illness as the sufferer, but without the recognition to go with it, or having much control over the situation. My analysis of such a relationship suggests to me that the burden on the Jasnas of the world is extremely heavy, and I am not surprised that marital breakdowns are quite common in such relationships. In the last section I reflect on all these changes and my revised view of life.

4.1 MENTALLY ACTIVE: WHILST I CAN

As for the impact on me physically, there are also many different aspects concerning the impact Parkinson's disease has had on my mental state and since they will take a lot of space to describe fully, I shall cover these in four sections: this section covers the need to be active, taking the theme 'whilst I can' and the next section continues the need to be active taking the theme 'activity, activity, activity'; the following two sections look at some unusual consequences under the two headings 'mind games' and 'mental enhancements'.

There are some things I started doing early on in my treatment which I believe were sub-conscious at the time although explicable to me now. In Chapter 2 I described how I kept going when I was clinically depressed sorting screws in the shed for hours at a time. I also started to buy DIY tools and materials and now my shed is jam packed with what appears to be a highly organised DIY and hardware store (it is not as organised as I would like, but we shall come to that later in this section). I probably have, for example 8 drill guns, of which 6 are cordless and vary in power, ability and price. Who can resist a high powered electric hammer drill for \$40 or £20? A bench drilling machine can be bought for only about twice that price. A ratchet set can be bought for half that price. Sanders, electric plane, circular saws, industrial SPS drill guns, routers etc; who can resist them all? Not me. Do I use all this equipment other than for the therapy that comes from repetitiously sorting them? I have put new doors in, added locks and opening handles to them, put security lamps on the house with the power supply going straight into the wall, built garden frames etc. I do not need anything like as much as I have got however, so why have I bought so much?

I believe sub-consciously I bought all these devices so that they are available to me to use whilst I still can, to seize the opportunity to use them to set against the day when I shall be incapable of doing anything with them. I have acquired them and used them "Whilst I can". Similarly I have over-acquired cleaning materials of all sorts, as well as stationery (to be discussed below). But another reason for purchasing all this 'stuff' is that it is ridiculously cheap with the advent of massive industrial production in China. Whereas when I was a boy tools were cared for because they were precise and expensive, it is probably more cost-effective to buy them, misuse them safely in any way necessary to get the job done, and if necessary throw them away and buy another. And so, why do I have six drills? Well, I can use one for drilling holes, a second for countersinking and a third for screw-driving...

Not long after Jasna and I set up house together we started going on holiday to an amazingly delightful hotel in Croatia, the Villa Giardino. A proper full description is given in the acknowledgements at the end of the book and I can only recommend the hotel to all (as long as I can still get in!). At the onset of Parkinson's disease we stopped going as much as we liked because the hotel is on a hill which can be fairly difficult to climb back up to from the sea even if you are fit.

But then I gave the matter some thought and suggested to Jasna in 2004 that we started going again. She was very surprised because my beach days had already sharply diminished by then (and are now non-existent) and the terrain is difficult for me to walk around. But we both love the place and it seemed to me that there would come a time soon enough when it may not be possible to make the journey and/or stay there in any meaningful way. I proposed that "Whilst I can" we should go nearly every year, which with the exception of this year we have done so far.

But there is a sort of irony about this decision and the writing of this book. After what is now called the Preface was written in 2003, I decided prompted by many readers of the Preface to write this book. And the book has largely been written whilst on holiday either at this hotel or at our other holiday hotel where we first met in 1988 near Dubrovnik (details again in the Acknowledgments) or whilst Jasna skis and I stay in the hotel to keep her company when not skiing. And the starting place was Villa Giardino in 2004. We have been every year since until this year and so successful is my ability to write there, that in 2007 I went to the hotel for a second visit in a month. I was on my own (Jasna had to work) but since most of the book has been written there, I returned on my own to see if I could get the manuscript near completion. Of the twelve writing holidays I have had so far, the five Villa Giardino visits account for over half of what had been written. A "Whilst I can" attitude obviously has its side benefits.

My need to 'preen' is probably a "Whilst I can" activity in that I enjoy giving advice and seminars, but I know I will not be able to do this for the rest of my life, especially the seminars. So I do these as frequently as I can, somewhere between 10 and 20 a year, and try to be as open and honest and controversial as I can "Whilst I can".

I bill myself as a Visiting Professor at the two universities, a pensioner and a discombobulator. The latter loosely translates as maverick, trouble maker, the small boy in the Emperor's New Clothes children's story who insists on telling it as he sees it. Anyone who knows me expects to hear exactly what I think. People seeking my advice know I shall give it without fear or favour. So if they do not want to hear the truth as I see it, they should not come and ask me for it.

4.2 MENTALLY ACTIVE: ACTIVITY, ACTIVITY, ACTIVITY

'Be not idle' is the best advice to avoid depression, but be not idle doing what? Activity of course, but without reflection, is the activity necessary or even desirable, or can it actually be detrimental?

What I am reasonably sure of is that the passing of time has lost the importance it used to have in my life. So now, I am always busy or occupied or 'fiddling about' or whatever label you choose to use. Deadlines and priorities are words I can explain the meaning of, but somehow they do not have much effect on me. I am easily absorbed by the activity I am doing, and I can then just as easily distract myself and be absorbed in another activity. Let me explain in the following explanatory box on Parkinson's disease FITness: the habit of Fiddling, Interfering or Tinkering (FIT).

Any activity I am engaged in will, therefore be followed relentlessly until – I bump into another activity. This then quickly becomes an established greater Interest than the one I am on so – on to the new activity, without fear or restraint. Birthday and Christmas cards are classic examples. I mean to send cards and presents, but they never rise into an active enough state where they get acted on.

Parkinson's disease FITness: the habit of Fiddling, Interfering or Tinkering (FIT).

I am very good at dealing with people – my brain is sharper in this sense than before treatment. But the following physical activities at a 'micro' level are all frustratingly slow to the point of exasperation: washing; dressing; handling paper; using a keyboard; packing or unpacking; sitting and getting up; and moving around in confined spaces.

I could be helped, but where is the balance between an appropriate level of self-sufficiency and giving up? Giving up is not natural to me, would lead to greater dependency as the ability to do these physical activities would diminish with lack of practice, and would allow melancholy sadness to stake its claim on my mind again.

So I do the best I can with as little help as possible – which still means: help with buttons occasionally; cutting of some foodstuffs on my plate (tough meat particularly); and I require the tolerance and patience of others in large measure.

But with an active brain and slow progress with micro movements, I have found the following to be true.

Paul's Conjecture of Parkinsonism FITness
"I am constantly moving from activity to activity as my brain, waiting for the body to catch up, entertains itself with a variety of thought leading to taking up a new activity whilst still not having completed the original. In other words I fiddle, interfere or tinker when left to my own devices".

I shall demonstrate how confusing and time consuming this tendency is by using the writing of this explanatory box as an example.

FITness Example
The first attempt to write this explanatory box actually started with my determination to finish writing an Editorial paper for a journal. This task was sidetracked by the need to make an analysis of journal issues per annum in order to make a point in the Editorial. The analysis in its turn was interrupted by the need to go to the bathroom. Whilst I was in the bathroom I stated to read a history book (one of my hobbies).

Whilst the book was good reading, the time being taken persuaded me to change the activity and start reading a paper I want to use in support of a view I have that "Statistical Packages Promote Promiscuous Statistical Relationships". Having decided to write this up immediately, I went straight to the computer file discussing the number of issues of the journal per annum as a sudden thought struck me that my previous calculations were false. Food and drink for lunch were also consumed, and music set up in the background.

This can easily be a typical work session if I do not keep focussed. As an outcome of thinking through the sequence of activities in the above example, it occurred to me that the reason I found completing anything very difficult could be encapsulated in the above conjecture, which is that my brain whilst waiting for dogsbody to catch up, keeps fiddling, interfering or tinkering and thus activity moves on.

And having formulated the conjecture, I then I decided to write this piece so that the conjecture was captured and could be incorporated in this book– and that decision rather confirms the conjecture!

And now? If only I knew ...!

Notes to this explanation.

1. The first attempt to write the Journal editorial was made on 24 July 2005, in my room in Hotel Croatia, Cavtat between 12.30 and 13.30 whilst Jasna was on the beach. And I promised to finish the Editorial paper by lunchtime – again! Jasna thinks I deliberately avoid the beach – but deliberation is not necessary! Lunch passed and nothing had been written.

2. Jasna read an early version of this box and told me it was very confusing. I have tried to make it more readable, but in some ways the confusion goes well with my state of mind when I am undertaking FITness.

This is the second reason for being late, a continual move from activity to activity which when I do get to assembling the material to take with me, means I can still easily be diverted by something I spot as I am sifting the materials. Given I was going to be late anyway for the physical effect reasons I gave in the previous chapter perhaps it is a surprise that I ever get anywhere.

Unconstrained I can easily drift, totally self-absorbed through a series of activities with nothing achieved and if I was doing that when Jasna goes to bed, the next thing I know is she appears and asks what were you doing all night? I have pointlessly meandered through activities all through the night. How is this book being written then? I am in my room at Villa Giardino on my own; I have little with me other than the book. I do have a book to read, but only one and this has to be eked out until I go home after two more days. Dancing, yes but there is only a certain amount of that you can do especially on your own. So I am more or less restricted to book writing!

Pre-Parkinson's disease diagnosis obsessions have sometimes become even more of an obsession, for example stationery. I love stationery for what it can do to organise you and help structure material for understanding and solution, and also for its own sake. But I find handling paper very difficult and when I am 'off', impossible. So I have experimented extensively and now a great many of my papers and paperwork are stored in presentation folders (usually plastic covers, preferably with stiff covers so they will stack vertically on shelves for ease of access. Very few people appreciate that there is any benefit to me as I seem to struggle to place the paper into the plastic holders in the presentation pack. Difficult to get in and maybe sometimes to get out but:

- All papers so stored are in quantities I can handle. Before I resorted to storing larger collections of paper in presentation files, I could spend a long time finding and manipulating paper to seek the items that I wanted. In such situations there was the potential added problem that some or all of the paper could slip from my variable grasp and end up randomly sorted for me on the floor. It is clear to me which method of handling paper is preferable.
- I can almost find any paper from such files more easily than before.

I have a lot more stationery and in some aspects, so much I cannot find what I want. But I also have other successes (from my point of view anyway). I now have nearly all my papers filed in presentation packs or in varying degrees of width/capacity plastic box files. The good thing about plastic filing is that it slides easily and the bad thing about it is that it slides easily!

Given my tendency to drift from activity to activity, it should be no surprise that few of the activities get done. In fact it is often suggested that nothing is ever finished but here you are reader, and this is my book I completed it in 2009 right before your very eyes.

But there are many things not finished. My study for example needs constant adjustment to handle the changing storage requirements. Or to put it another way, it is always under construction (improvement in my view). I have started to fill in forms for my benefit entitlements many times but finished none of them in less than four years. Is this non-completion or denial?

I have 'started' 11 books, but effectively seriously only about 4 have actually started, and none had been finished until this one. I have endless ideas but without someone following behind moving the seed onto fertile ground, then most will stay where they are on stony ground. And in section 4.5 below the progress of the journal I am an editor of is discussed including its frequent lateness of sending material to the publisher – the same story again.

On the other hand, this section gives the impression of constant non completions. Internet shopping brings in many good products and services which the household benefits from. The journal I just mentioned is bigger, better and increasing in sales in a contracting market. This book was written. My affairs are increasingly in better order and we are not poor, in part due to my management of our finances. I have adopted a meta-activity which is to control activity drift!

4.3 MIND GAMES

I have already mentioned by ability not to get enough sleep, and most people are aware that sleep deprivation is a form of torture in some parts of the world. Most people are also aware that some mentally ill people hear 'voices', see apparitions and so on. In this sub-section I am going to describe my experiences in this arena.

If I stay awake all night and do not go to sleep the next day, then I am ready for my eyes to play 'tricks' on me. When the light is poor during the second evening, any shapes captured in the corners of my eyes suddenly take on human forms regardless of what they are. I guess this is my tired eyes and brain seeking first order recognition and I guess people would rank high in any sensible ranking list (because they might be your loved ones or because they might be dangerous).

If I was tired already before staying awake all night then any movement of the head or eyes is likely to conjure up human forms at any instant of the eye refocusing. And if as I did once, you do not go to bed at a reasonable time the following night then very strange things can happen. I have 'tried' this once by drifting rather than going to bed (Jasna was away). It is hard for me to capture the full effects of the human beings coming towards me one after the other or in groups, non-stop until I closed my eyes. And my brain suggested that these were my ancestors come to tell me...? Well, they were an ugly lot, so maybe they were my ancestors. I went fearfully to bed and I have never allowed myself to sink that low again.

And there are sounds to be heard as well. When I am particularly tired I have noticed that small noises, say from an electrical appliance (when it's off, but still connected to the power socket and there is a light electric 'hum') can easily be misheard as music in the background, like a radio playing music quietly in another room. Sometimes the music is more of a conversation.

So there you have it, I hear voices and see non-existent see-through people, and some of you always knew I had long gone! But seriously, it's amazing that anyone should expect any system not to behave strangely if it is abused, worked past its tolerances, generally not looked after. I wonder how many people labelled with same form of mental illness are just in need of proper attention to their body. You may think this observation farfetched and of course mental illness is not confused with physical malfunctioning in the way I suggest here. But before you say how simplistic my comments are, just recall the recent revelation in the last 10 to 20 years that single women who became pregnant found themselves in mental institutions for life in some countries. If one can sort out family shame by locking up a pregnant unmarried daughter in a mental institution, what chance that an inarticulate individual who hears voices and sees non-existent people is going to avoid a similar fate?

Another abuse of one's body which has severe effects for Parkinson's sufferers is to overdo the effort put into some activity, which usually goes hand in hand with sleep deprivation. For example, I have had massive reconstruction work done to my house recently. This involved the hire of a building company, planning applications, building regulations, stress engineers, party wall surveyors, the raising of finance and cost negotiations. During the course of all this turmoil, it became clear that my credit rating was 0! A 'mistake' had been made on my record 4 years ago by a credit card company, and although it was all sorted out eventually, there was an extra 2 months of finance uncertainty. Meanwhile, I was busy clearing parts of the house and finding new storage places for the materials, usually conducted at speed (to overcome small movement problems) for several hours at a time. The net result was a series of hyper-ventilation/panic attacks. The solution was to sleep more, but the point is that a sufferer with a disease like Parkinson's does not have the reserves, mental or physical, to put excess effort into projects in the same way as a fit person can get away with (for a while)!

I take a plethora of pills throughout the day, with a regular combination every two and a half hours. It is surprisingly difficult to remember every two and a half hours on the dot. But the downside is that if too much delay occurs, the sufferer will go 'off', usually for a time proportional to the delay. In any case, a conscious effort needs to be maintained to check on the medications' effectiveness, recording all untoward happenings which the doctor needs to know about in order to match medication to need. This is a tremendous overhead on mental activity and means a sufferer cannot get away from the disease for much more than an hour at a time. This encourages an approach to life that is totally self-absorbing. This is why I voluntarily help at two universities, to avoid my world shrinking down me.

Monitoring drug effectiveness is also necessary for when other external forces take a hand in your life. An example which is perhaps obvious when you know, but unlikely to occur to you until you do, is the effect of other sickness like the common cold on a Parkinson's sufferer. It appears as far as I can tell that the body's mechanisms for fighting a common cold attacks anything likely to be the cause and that come from outside the system – like my medicine! I had a cold in late 2006 which was so effectively attacked by my bodies' defences that my medicine was wiped out within an hour or two of intake. For a week my ability to move was greatly restricted, at its lowest point to less than two hours for three times a day. If that level of mobility is where I am heading...

4.4 MENTAL ENHANCEMENTS

We have observed that in spite of my high drug intake, simple things like dealing with paper and shirts are a problem. But the drugs have improved my raw brain power which I see evidence of in two ways. First when driving my car I am conscious that my road awareness, always quite good, is even better with the net effect of a faster thinking ahead speed.

Second, whilst I have always been fast in seeing solutions to problems, connecting different ideas together beneficially and winning arguments, I am now much better at these things than I was before. And because I am so quick and relaxed, I give the impression of supreme self confidence which people seem to find reassuring. I am quite confident in the same way as Talleyrand who, when asked about his confidence, replied "When I examine myself, I worry. When I compare, I am reassured". People come to me with their problems, often upset, and they usually leave much happier.

I have acquired with increasing skill the ability to look at a problem and to express the basics of the problem in simple terms. For example, PhD students who have come for my advice towards the end of their PhD have often said after an hour's conversation that they had learnt more about the business of getting a PhD in that time than in the whole of their PhD so far.

I have also noticed that my seminar audiences over the past few years often appear entirely enrapt when I speak. So much so that several times I have suggested that I feel like a lamp, and my audiences are all rabbits, transfixed as they stare at me the lamp. Three of my seminars have been recorded and I must admit I was shocked at my performance. Relaxed, confident, in command of the material, even I thought I should believe what I heard being said!

And I can also be on time if I consider it essential. This I achieve by ceasing all activity except getting ready well in advance and taking supplementary medicine to make sure I will not go 'off'. So why cannot I always do this? Because this effort is exceptional and I do not wish to taking medicine outside the prescribed boundaries fixed by my consultant.

So this section has shown that not everything about having Parkinson's disease is negative, although the balance of gains to losses is clear.

4.5 MY IMPACT ON OTHER PEOPLES' MENTAL STATES

I am on full sickness benefit retirement, which will be discussed in section 6.2, does not permit me to take paid employment.

Fig. 2: Maturing

Fig. 1: Early days

Fig. 3: Wedding

Fig. 4: Going down

Fig. 5: Food for thought, checking the proofs

Fig. 6: Jasna - AHA (A Higher Authority)

Fig. 7. The author (standing, right) and co-author, Frank Fenner (seated, left).

Fig. 8: Always dancing

But my medical advisers recommend that I work as much as I can as therapy. So I work on a voluntary basis for my only two employers in my life, Brunel University and the London School of Economics (what I whimsically call my basket weaving activities, my form of therapy). There are many advantages to this arrangement. I only do what I like doing. I only do as much as I want to. It gives structure to my life, purpose and fulfils my deep innate need to interact with people. When pressed by Jasna on this latter need, I initially gave obvious answers such as I like to help people. But I have to admit, the honest reason is I believe because I like preening myself in public.

I am usually late for appointments (the reasons for this are discussed in the section 4.2 above) or sometimes I fail to turn up at all that day. Nobody complains about me, since my services are given free. And, from the feedback I get, my advice and support is generally well valued. I am largely treated with respect and affection, a sort of deified venerable mascot. I am good at giving advice, so people come to me with their problems. Retired with an incurable disease, I am very relaxed about everyday life problems that other people have. I deal with them with detachment and confidence. The more problems I help with, the better I get. The better I get with helping people, the more people come, the better I get … I expect to continue giving advice to people in this way until I am past my 'sell-by date'. It is a pleasure to take a stream of confused unhappy people and work with them so that they leave more personally knowledgeable and contented.

When I took retirement I expected to have to relinquish my rather pleasant office at Brunel University.

But it turned out to be true that I would do more from that office on a voluntary basis than many a full-time employee!

There are difficulties and questions about my voluntary activities. If I can do all the above activities, why not get paid for it? But that would undermine my personal sense of security as I explain in Chapter 6, so I would be less effective. And who would pay someone to be regularly late or absent? An advantage of not being paid is that I can speak my mind clearly and openly and do not have to follow some University policy line. Whilst this means that everyone can expect of me only honesty, this would be easier for some to handle if I only spoke when spoken to - but I do not. The managers of the departments I visit have a problem with me in that most of them have known me for some time, and quite a fair number would even admit to being one of my protégés, so they find it hard to argue with me let alone say no. They should say no if they believe their position to be the correct position (they are after all responsible for what they are the appointed manager of, not me) but I am a difficult person to argue with (I am very experienced!). I cannot just go along and give advice when asked for – I have to offer it whatever it is and whenever I feel it is needed.

It is not in my nature to be content with the current state of an organisation. Standing still has no attraction for me since I believe from all I have experienced that standing still leads to decline. So I constantly suggest, challenge, provoke and sometimes call meetings to move things forward, to improve our business (teaching, researching, disseminating, critiquing), to seek continuous improvement in the quality of everything we do. I once described my Department as large, wealthy and comfortable. And that being comfortable was a worry to me with respect to the future.

After six years of advice giving and casting shadows over the current managers, a new phenomenon has come about. More recent appointments as managers act as though if I give them advice and they take it, this will demean them in the community and label them as just agents for me. So they have tended in increasing numbers to do the opposite of what I recommend. I think they assume that this will improve their stature. Such immediate short term thinking is very common especially with new managers who by and large start their managerial careers by making any of a number of classic mistakes (in my view). The two most common mistakes a new manager makes is to order many uninformed changes to the systems that are in use, and the placing of petty controls on their staff to show they are the boss. These approaches signify insecurity – a good manager does not need to be demonstratively doing things which leads to these classic mistakes. Recognition is to do with how well what is being managed is performing, not about the manager, and not about the manager making trivial decisions.

If a long term view is taken however, then the above actions would be seen as being potentially seriously damaging. Uninformed changes are more likely to make things worse, and controlling staff usually reduces the benefits associated with responsibility that allows flexibility and adaptability when required. On the other hand, following good advice means that you will be more successful and as you become increasingly surrounded by success you will eventually and inevitably get the blame for all the success! In any case all success is claimed by everyone, and failure whether through deliberately not taking good advice will inevitably be credited to you alone.

One of my successful protégés has got our relationship sorted out well. He asks me frequently, sometimes two or three times a week for my advice, considers it carefully, decides what to use and what he disagrees with. This seems to work very well for him, and from what I can see, he is very successful. A second successful protégé I only see in passing when out and about and she seems so lost she is considering moving out of the University to another job. A third successful protégé is visibly not doing as well as he has done, but never asks. We discuss matters if I arrange a meeting, but I have stopped doing that since he needs to find his own way, which might include coming back to me for advice.

So in spite of some immediate success with what I have tried to teach, long term benefits to individuals are very individual. My impact is not consistently evident from their mental deliberations. This is one reason why one of my other autobiographical books will be on Leading and Managing People (The LAMP approach). I hope to share my experiences with a wider audience since many of my lessons are at one level obvious, but not as widely practiced as they should be. One of my colleagues for 20 years pointed out to me that when I was in a room giving advice to any number of people it all seemed clear and straightforward. Apparently when I have departed it does not take long for this clarity to fade away. So if my experience is to be useful it needs to be written up – just as for this book.

One day I know it will be time for me to move on. As I write this text it is six years since I retired. I am amazed I am still around, although as noted above, patience with me is thinning. But I am cautious, so I am determined to finish writing this book in 2009 and maybe from that start a successful autobiographical book series to keep me professionally busy.

On the personal front PhD students still come to me in large numbers for advice. Nowadays they have got used to me dancing in front of them, and a few of them will join in. Having completed 55 PhDs under my supervision and given advice and examined a further several hundred (maybe towards a thousand all together) it can take me only 20 to 40 minutes to uncover and explain to a usually astonished student the major weaknesses in the text and how to remedy them effectively and efficiently. Since I often dance whilst reading the text, this adds to the mystique. But there is no magic; it is like the apocryphal story about a golfer who hit a hole-in-one during a tournament. A spectator called out "lucky strike" and the player retorted "yes it was lucky, and the more I practice the luckier I get!"

I have recently for three years been Editor-in-Chief of one of the leading academic research journals in the field of Information Systems, called the *European Journal of Information Systems*. I was one of the founders of the journal 20 years ago, but have played a back seat role until formal retirement gave me the time to lead the journal. Table 5 below shows that the pagination of the journal has more or less doubled in the last two years compared to just three years ago, with 2007'ss volume 16 well in excess of 800 pages. There is a myth that limiting supply increases quality and that increasing supply reduces quality. I believe that the quality of published papers has also risen for the following reasons.

Table 5. Data for the European Journal of Information Systems for four years/volumes

Year	Volume	Pages	Number of issues
2004	13	336	4
2005	14	525	5
2006	15	664	6
2007	16	800 plus	6

We have a well established refereeing process where papers are put out to an Associate Editor who finds two referees to help review the submission and its revisions until publication or rejection. The only change in this quality aspect of the *European Journal of Information Systems* is the increasing number of volunteers we get who want to be Associate Editors because it will be good experience and help their career. In other words, it is because they wish to work with and be associated with a quality journal. And being ambitious, they tend to be very effective at reviewing for the same reason. So I perceive the general papers to be of improving interest and quality.

The *European Journal of Information Systems* has moved to 6 issues a year for the last two years and every issue has either been a Special Issue or had a Special Section in it. We have rarely asked for special issues to be proposed to us, they come in of their own motivation. So whereas two years ago in 4 issues we did not always have such content in each issue, now the demand to guest edit is clearly rising. This can only be career beneficial if guest editing is for a quality journal, so I take market forces to be another positive indicator. And lastly the recent introduction of opinion papers are starting to encourage authors to write their own opinion papers as readers find these papers more interesting and readable in general. I consider that to be a mark of quality too.

Whilst as in all things that I do I have generally been late getting issues of the journal to the publisher, with much anguish all round, the improvements to the journal do show that a Parkinson's sufferer can still make a contribution to Society in some form or another, although it may take some imagination to find the contribution. I am leading a campaign to look at what the Information Systems discipline is about, and how it can be usefully researched, again an activity that requires effort but not to a very tight time schedule (partly because I am driving it)! So in conclusion, because of my involvement, the other people involved in the production of the journal have a much more volatile working pattern than other journal workers.

In all these activities I am looked after wherever I go. Probably the best example is how my bags are taken from me and carried whenever people who know me bump into me. This is ironic as I explain in my Packing and Carrying Bags Vignette below. People try to help but they do not know how. Perhaps this book will help.

In the Departments at Brunel University and the LSE I have found everyone to be supportive. But there are some who make extra special efforts to help me, such as: Edgar Whitley at LSE, ex-student, ex-colleague and friend;

The Packing and Carrying Bags Vignette

For nearly three and a half years after my self-diagnosis I did not tell anyone at work about my condition. I made a mess of packing my bags at the end of the day and people just helped as a matter of course. Then, when I made my illness public, I suddenly and to this day are deemed unable to carry my bags anymore and they are removed from me as soon as it is spotted I am carrying them. I protest that I will be left a weakling if this continues since I am not being allowed to exercise muscles. Of course there are occasions when I am not feeling so well and then bag carrying is a must if I am 'off'. On the other hand through no fault of theirs people do not know what I need and it is not easy to say so. I went on a trip for a few days to a University far enough away to require me to stay at a hotel for two days.

My host, bright and thoughtful insisted on my bags being carried everywhere. But each morning he was clearly annoyed that I left my room way after the time he agreed to pick me up (and I missed breakfast). What he did not know was the time it takes me to sort my papers and clothes, and pack and dress. I am dreadfully slow, but I did not feel one of his students should be sent to pack my clean and dirty clothes.

Tillal Eldabi and Alan Serrano at Brunel University, former PhD students, colleagues and friends who keep an eye on me and even visit me at home to do this; and

Carole Bromley whose role as my secretary I shall cover in chapter 6. Here I shall cover some of her personal attributes which have affected me as a Parkinson's sufferer and how my way of thinking has had a great influence on her.

Carole is also a little different to most people. She is a medium or white witch. She knows things about people that surprise them when told. Carole has taken serious commissions from reputable bodies. The BBC covered one of her investigations at a 'haunted' building. The building in question was the rope house at the Naval Dockyard at Devonport, England which Carole investigated at the request of the Naval Commander. Ropes were produced in vast quantities for 18th and 19th century ships, and the rope house was one of the sources of manufacture. It was also the place of execution by hanging of condemned sailors many years ago. Carole took a team of mediums, and invited a scientific team to join her. A third team was of navy personnel. In the early hours of the morning these three groups wandered around the house, and all reported strange lights, doors closing with no one near and many other unusual things.

The scientific team could not record any of this with any of their equipment. So they declared that the mediums found spirits because that was what they were looking for, but in their view there was no evidence because they had not recorded anything. I helped Carole respond by pointing out that it was no more scientific to assume something isn't there, observe inexplicable happenings and then conclude nothing was there just because the equipment you have is inadequate to record what you saw.

I am not a believer in 'ghosts' and 'Spirits' – nor a disbeliever. As a Parkinson's sufferer there are many things happening to me for which we have no explanation. It is said that everything we know about what the brain does accounts for a quarter of its volume. So what does the rest do? With that level of knowledge about us, I believe one should be wary of assuming that people who have an unusual understanding are necessarily imposters. What I do not know dwarfs infinitely the little I do know. Carole gives me challenges that make me think more about these things. We are contemplating a debating book on the subject. In the meantime, Carole was incentivised by my writing this book, and decided to emulate my history telling. But she has not just emulated the idea, but her book appeared in print some months before mine! (Carole Bromley 2009, The Living Spirit, AuthorHouse, Milton Keynes). I expect that joint publications will start to emerge with the success of our individual ventures.

In spite of my weakness with paper, there are still people who give me paper and when we next meet expect me to have read it! In fact giving me any paper does not mean as they think that I will go home and carefully read it. It just joins a huge amount of unread paper. And if they are amazingly optimistic they expect me to bring the copy they gave me appropriately marked up and do not bring another copy at all with them. So we have no material to discuss. And people still send me emails and expect me to type long replies!

But all in all, I am privileged by my colleagues' behaviour toward me. In July 2007 it was my 60th birthday and I was told that my ex-Faculty staff were taking me out to lunch. Fortunately I began to get increasingly suspicious and wrote an 'impromptu' speech just in case! Sure enough when I arrived at the Department to meet with my hosts, a band was unloading its instruments and there was food and drink and a very large number of colleagues who had turned up on a University vacation day to wish me Happy Birthday. Some attended from as far afield as Manchester, which was very surprising. The birthday cake was designed as an iPod with two speakers such was the time and effort put into the event.

I cannot deny that I rather like the affection and respect I get as I go about my basket weaving!

4.6 MENTAL MATE AND CARER

I asked Jasna my wife for her views on the mental effects of me having Parkinson's disease and fortunately she got tired before her imagination ran out. Jasna is obviously nearer to me than any other human being and sees me frequently daily. So her comments might reveal things about me that I overlook. But this is my autobiography. So I shall add my observations to her comments, even though I know I shall be accounting for them at length until I see things properly (plus ca change!). I have tabulated the comments and my responses for ease of reference. When Jasna looked at the table, she thought it looked like any domestic argument, and could not see the contribution to the book. I agree that the style of comment and response is of a domestic argument style, but that the things being argued about are a little unusual and Parkinson's disease specific. I shall be brief here because the main value of these comments is that they show the enormous pressure that Carers can be put under and not the points themselves.

Table 6. Jasna's comments and my responses

Jasna's comments	My response
Sorting, sorting, sorting. Filing, filing, filing but not doing. Keeps reorganising the shed and study which might be OK if the stored material were not packed so tight it cannot be got out! Always emptying and rearranging his bag. Disorder in everyday things.	Already agreed to above in this chapter if not quite in these words
Internet shopping another way of avoiding activity.	Maybe, but isn't shopping just that at one level?
Can't stop fidgeting, drives her up the wall.	Me too
Needs to please everyone all the time, generous with gifts and tips.	I have never found that treating other people well is a disadvantage
I have become less tolerant with her, easily become irritated, aggressive and making her less tolerant. More easily irritated than I used to be and especially by Jasna, and can be quite aggressive and never used to be.	I can't answer absurd questions and can't even be bothered trying any more. "Why didn't you do it this way?" Because I didn't!
Obsessively buys a shoe cleaning kit every trip	Having been forbidden once and since the cost is £1 to £2 it is now compulsory for me – and my shoes are clean.

Argumentation is no longer logical she says but she would wouldn't she?	I don't remember ever being told it was
Barely copes, always starting things and never ending them	Which is why dear reader this book does not exist!
Changes computer too often, files a mess.	I am finishing this book on a great new machine!

Well I asked. Some of these comments by Jasna I have recorded here even though I consider them to be just a gaming tactic to keep me in order. All in all they do not look encouraging for our relationship. Alternatively, one could say that we have an incredibly strong relationship to survive the reality behind the comments.

JASNA THE CARER
First one has to understand how easy I am to deal with. I am the middle child of three siblings which meant as far as I can see that I had to fight for my share of attention at a very early age. Jasna would say that I am an attention seeker using the method of trying to please people. But it is not that simple.

Professionally I have vision where most people do not; I am a man of creative ideas and a natural leader. I have determination to the point of obstinacy and if I consider myself right, I never give up. In other words I am very difficult, especially to argue with. So whoever is close to me has a fairly difficult time frequently. For example when I was a Dean, my boss argued against one of my intentions for 20 minutes at a meeting he held with the Deans. Then he said *"I don't know why I am arguing with you, you will do it anyway won't you."* There was only one answer available to me.

One of my Personal Assistants once informed me that she would hate to be my wife. Fair enough, although I had never suggested she should be! In chapter five I describe how early apparently I was like this, as seen in the 60th birthday party revelation vignette (section 5.6).

So I am a difficult possibly tough partner to have. But then Jasna is no shrinking violet either. I offer you some of her views on males in the next Vignette below.

But enough of this type of material and the comments in table 6. As I said in Chapter 2, the carer in some ways suffers more. Let me explain.

When I am down or 'off' or in any way unwell, I am to some extent aware of the nature, possibly the cause and to some extent how I might remedy the situation. But all Jasna sees is the manifestation of the problem. It hurts to see it, it hurts to be reminded for the millionth time that I have Parkinson's disease, and it hurts that she often cannot find a way to help me, which causes guilt at letting me down, which she then resents.

My methods of dealing with my problems are, because of my determination, whatever it takes. This is fine for me because I am making the choice, but for Jasna to see me dancing in a public place on my own, quite energetically and not over-elegantly, is not a choice she made. Nor can she easily tell me not to do it, because she admires and encourages my determination to fight, but why do I have to do it this way and so publicly?

OK so I have found some methods that help me that are unorthodox, and now like a missionary I would like to proselytise them loudly and often. This is never a role in life she would choose for herself, but she cannot disprove of me doing it because I am sort of heroic – at least many people believe I am and say so. But they do not have to live with me or partner non-stop heroism day in day out.

Jasna's Views on Males Vignette

I like to tell females if I have not told them before (and I don't mind repeating either) that:
Women are more intelligent than men
Women are multitasking
Women are stronger than men (no man could have a baby)
Women live longer than men.
Their only weakness is a fondness for men
Thank God for that

Most women are amused, flattered and pleased with me when I tell them this.
When I told Jasna she just said matter-of-facedly "I knew that"
Someone once commented that she obviously believed in sexual equality to which she replied "I see no reason to raise men to my level".
When interviewed for her first academic post in England, she was asked why there were more men than women in computing. "Because men are natural hackers" she replied.
I used to tell a joke which went "how can you tell when a man has a wife more intelligent than he?" to which the witty answer was "he thinks he is in charge!" But the joke lost its punch line when Jasna pointed out that all wives are more intelligent than their husbands.

> At a conference a male delegate tried to impress her and singularly failed. He announced his despair and suggested he felt like going out to the nearby rocky coast and bashing himself against the rocks. Go ahead she suggested (he became and remains a good friend)!

So she is caught in between my desires, people's responses and her beliefs, and the latter whilst as valid as anyone else's can seem churlish if expressed.

I took early retirement because I felt insecure with my bosses obviously being unsupportive to be charitable, or personally vindictive if you take a paranoid view (I don't). Even if the middle ground of just making a mess is assumed (which I agree with), I took sickness retirement in the belief that I could not handle the job anymore. I feel in retrospect that retiring was the right decision, the job was killing me. It took more than two years to look better again. But Jasna dreaded my retiring, cutting me off from those aspects of the job I really enjoyed: pressured action and decision making, wielding power and responsibility with enthusiasm and effectively. And as can be seen from the comments in table 6, her fears about what would then happen to me if I retired seem to have been borne out.

Jasna is on track with her career. She has been promoted to Professor four years after my retirement, and is now Head of Department. Both these roles are very time consuming and sometimes she comes home tired. And her retired husband greets her with disorder in the house.

Trying to run my life as if I do not have Parkinson's disease is clearly the right thing to do, and people who do not know cannot usually tell. So if I look normal why cannot I do all the normal things? If I looked as ill as I am, everyone would know I was ill, and the expectations of all and sundry would reflect this, and also influence Jasna therefore.

To summarise, Jasna has a tough job, a tough husband, and he has a tough illness for her to worry about. She isn't always happy with me not surprisingly, but here we are in our tenth year together since diagnosis, which is almost as long as we had pre-diagnosis (ten years). I was lucky to meet her, I was lucky to get her, and I am lucky to still have her. And I still love her. What she gets out of it I have no idea. If she is not a hero, then there are no heroes.

4.7 REFLECTING MENTALLY

Michael J Fox calls his Parkinson's disease autobiography *Lucky Man*. I do not agree, I do not feel I am lucky at all. On the other hand, I do not feel particularly unlucky either. I am alive (many do not see 60 years), I am functioning (there are many disabling or quick killing illnesses far worse than mine), I am not poor, and I have affection and friendship. So I have Parkinson's disease? Well I would rather not, but I was never offered an option, I have it, it won't go away, so get on with it. I understand Michel J Fox's view that Parkinson's disease gave him the chance to look at his life and one outcome has been the highly creditable Michael J Fox Foundation for Parkinson's Research which raises very respectable income for sponsoring many different research avenues. It would be no surprise to me if he is remembered for the foundation long after his acting has been forgotten (good though that is).

I have never looked forward to retirement; in fact I had hoped to retire after 65 at 70 say. I loved my job and I always held in hope the belief that I might somehow or another make a contribution to mankind. Perhaps this book is going to do that. And then maybe the full seven autobiographies? But if not, then I shall enjoy ideas, read about them, and write even if only for myself. I reason if there is a God, it still makes sense to enjoy your life. And if death is death, which I can find no refuting evidence for, then it would be foolish to do anything else other than to enjoy your life!

And is it necessary to be remembered for something? When my Mum died a few years ago, I stayed up all night to write a funeral speech. I was shocked thinking about it for the first time at just what a good person she was:

> *"She was not ... even a professor. But if there were many less or even none of these people, and more people or even everyone was like Kath, what a peaceful honest pleasant world we would live in."*

> *" .. she ... as far as I know never deliberately hurt anyone."*

How many people do you know that the last quote can be said of?

But how will posterity benefit from her past actions? Well, this book to start with. And the role model she was for so many people. When I help people and they express great gratitude, I ask them what they have learnt from our discussion. "Oh, how wonderful you are .." which I agree with of course and then go on to point out that the real lesson is that one day they will be in a position to help others as I do, and if we all did that, the world would be a better place.

Am I a better person because I have Parkinson's disease? I don't think so. But maybe through this book I will help more people than I ever would if I had not been ill. Certainly Jasna and Carole and many more believe this to be true. What does this contribute to my desire to know "who am I?", or put more generally, "who are we? I cannot say I have found the answer, or anything approaching it. But maybe I am trying too hard. Maybe the answer to the question "who are we?" is quite simple and does not require lots of thought. Maybe the answer is just "who we are".

CHAPTER 5

PEOPLE AND PARKINSON'S DISEASE

In this chapter I describe people's reactions to my illness, first when I went public starting with the family in 2002 and then colleagues and friends in 2003, and then reactions subsequently once the situation had settled down. Of course most people are sympathetic and encouraging, but I like to think that people's real feelings can be gauged only after a certain amount of time has elapsed.

I distinguish between family and friends because the first you are born into or acquire (by marriage) and the second you select. Clearly the family is very supportive, and I tell some stories about this. Friends, relatives and acquaintances are more volatile because they come and go for career purposes or greater challenges. Not all reactions were positive, but the vast majority were. I have included some quotes from colleagues so that the reader can gauge the sincerity of the writers for themselves. If you think I should be flattered by what is written, you would be entirely right.

5.1 THE QUESTION MANY WANT TO ASK

This chapter is about the way a variety of people in my life reacted when I told them the news about my Parkinson's disease. I did not tell anyone at all after telling Jasna on 1 January 2000 until I told my children during the summer of 2002. Of course my medical support knew, but no one else. And no one suspected anything, although retrospectively some claim to be able to post-match what they remember with the revelation (mostly that at the end of a long day I looked tired – and so did they).

The reason no one suspected is for the same reason some people ask the question that I can see many others are curious about nowadays. My mother-in-law, through Jasna interpreting, went route one on the question very early after I went public. With no hesitation it came thus:

"How come if you are so ill, that you look so well?"

Good question. I do not like being ill (no one does, but I am exasperated by it). I largely make the minimum concessions to my illness. Since professional life is a game to me, I keep playing whatever the circumstances (the only exception as I have always said being my salary - that is really serious!). The advantage of this approach is that game playing well is important, more so than winning or losing – but play to win. So determine the nature of the games you are involved in, which means looking systemically at your world, work out what you want from the game and then work out how to get it. This approach should not just as it stands be particularly successful except for one small thing. Bye and large, very few people take this approach so the chances are you are one of a few, or even just one, who has looked at what is going on in any structured way. So you win more often than you should. And when you sometimes lose, it's only a game. And there will be another day.

Taking this approach to work leaves you generally able to keep calm whilst all around you are losing their heads, to think logically and unemotionally and to generally sound more sensible than most. I am known for being imperturbable and creative in my thinking. So when I was diagnosed and even when I had clinical depression, I still treated work as a set of games, and no one had any reason to think anything about me beyond my usual sound if not excellent performance.

I also hid any physical manifestation of my illness at all times and I was well supported in this by my medication. And in the family and among friends this was also important, since game playing is not appropriate for the people you love.

Here the prevailing factor was that I was the Head of the Family as far as everyday practical things were concerned. Of course for part of my family, my Dad being most senior is titular Head and similarly there are other titular Heads for other married-in parts of the Big family and even more so for friends. But when it came to seeking advice invariably people came to me, and since the advice was at least sound if not impressive, my position was never in question. And before coming out, nothing in terms of the advice I gave or my physical appearance gave a clue that anything had changed.

But what happens if you are suddenly very ill? Are you dumped, venerated, ignored, loved or what? In this chapter I explain what I think happened when I came out and since. The next four sections are to do with the moment of telling people and the immediate aftermath. The last two sections explain how I think I am perceived now.

5.2 TELLING THE FAMILY

I told my daughter Ruth first. She had given birth to my fantastic non-identical twin grandsons Phoenix and Elliot on I June of that year 2002, and I felt that she and her husband were entitled to know the family medical ancestry – in fact of course two years earlier would have been more appropriate. I had not told anyone since Jasna two and a half years before and so I was quite emotionally wound up. Ruth has always been very precious to me, so I told Ruth in an excessively emotional way. Though she was taken aback, like many in my family, starting with my dad, bad news seems to have no immediate impact – and that is because we go straight into shock.

I phoned a few days later and she said she was OK and sounded it. What about my medical news I asked? Her reply quite threw me. She said I started telling her in such a state she was preparing for the worst, cancer and death in six months or something like that. When she found out it was Parkinson's disease she was almost relieved! Well that is one way of making bad news palatable, start by making it seem much worse and then relief takes over when it is not so serious! Everything is after all relative!

My son Benjamin had belatedly become used to the idea that I was married to Jasna, meeting her for the first time at a dinner in honour of my 50th birthday in 1997, over seven years since Jasna and I set up home together.

There is a belief in the family that I feel less for my son than for my daughter – nonsense, I love and am proud of them both beyond words. A father and son do not always show this as emotionally as they should. Imagine my pleasure when Benjamin decided to bond with me after I told him my news and we spent two individual days together that year. I am not sure exactly what we did, but I revelled in the time with him.

Next up were my older brother David who lived in France and my younger sister Mary who lives on the island of Anglesey on the west coast of Wales. They were shocked and then they independently said they both wanted to come and see me and they meant it and did. I was surprised, what was all the fuss about? I can be quite stupid sometimes. I was their role model if you like, the successful brother, the first to go to University, be an academic, and become a Professor and then Head of Department and lately Dean. The golden boy, for whom nothing was impossible, suddenly struck down. They came, separately, and I told them some things, and they followed me around, and I asked them if there was anything else they wanted me to tell them and there was not and I kept wondering why they had come. As I said a few lines above, quite stupid sometimes.

I had lived with my illness for two and a half years, it was news to them. Whilst I knew they loved me, I had not thought about it in terms of how much, if you can measure such things. On reflection, their visits showed how inward looking I had become, and just how much they really did love me (expressed even more forcefully as told in section 5.6 by David on another occasion). If I had given it wiser thought I would have realised that if the situation had been reversed I would have been visiting them as soon as possible. I had forgotten my own lessons on seeing the other person's point of view.

My Dad was 83 by this time and I did not really want to tell him – no parent likes to hear such news about any of their children. But as the pool of informed people grew larger, it would be inevitable that he would come to hear about it, probably out of context, explained as well as the informant was capable, but not as well as the most informed, me. And at the moment of discovery, who could he ask questions of? My brother David agreed we should do it together, so he arranged to see our Dad and I picked him up from the airport and we arrived on Dad's doorstep. My father is no fool and he sensed something out of the ordinary with the welcoming greeting, "Oh, the *two* of you". We chatted and lunched and the three of us found ourselves in one of Dad's sheds surrounded by the hoarded bric-a-brac of centuries which Dad was sure he would find a use for in good time. We showed him a router, and in the middle of discussing this machine I gently told him as best I could. As mentioned above, genetics kicked in and he went quiet as he went into shock. He said something about there is always a dark cloud on the horizon, or something always pops up whenever you start to think things might be getting better – and then he returned back to talking about the router!

A few hours later, without displaying any outward perturbation at any time, he suddenly started asking questions and from there, now that he was ready, we discussed it with him. Now he is 89, but he looks upon me as the relatively physically disadvantaged. As I have said elsewhere, my Dad is a hero to me.

There is a similar tale of disorientation for my Mum (now sadly deceased) when she was told. Mum is the lady who brought me up from the age of 7 when my mother left for greener pastures forever in Australia. There was no way Mum could take it in, but she had some heart problems of her own for which she was taking Warfarin. "I'm a game old bird, they have to give me rat poison!" she said. And she was.

Of course I told my mother in Australia too. It was one of those ironies that the month I diagnosed myself started with my only ever trip to Australia to see my mother and my Ozlings (the affectionate name I give to the Australian batch of two boys and a girl to match the English batch of myself and my brother and sister). They had all been to England in recent years, my mother twice to bury her parents (and I had picked her up the first time at Heathrow Airport not having seen her for over 20 years when I was seven. Was that my mother, is she my mother, But it was obvious when she actually did appear), and I wanted to see them in situ. Some people like to feel that nothing skips their attention, so I guess that might account for mother and the Ozlings being the only people ever who thought there might be something wrong with me on the basis of travelling all around the world without a stopover and spending a week with them. I maintain a measure of contact appropriate for the interest shown.

5.3 TELLING FRIENDS

Most of my friends are also colleagues, but I distinguish between those that are friends and those who are just colleagues The latter are discussed in the next section.

But the first friend I told was Beverley Ford of Springer-Verlag London who had worked with me on computing book series, now defunct and therefore we met occasionally out of friendship. At yet another of her splendid pub lunches I told her my situation in 2003. She was quite shocked, but more unexpectedly she tells me she has a sense of pride since I told her that she was the first friend to know. She has never forgotten the moment I told her, nor the honour she feels I bestowed on her.

The second person was a friend, colleague and protégé, Rob Macredie, who was also one of my Heads of Department for the Faculty I was Dean of. I wanted to tell him because by June 2003 I had decided to take sickness retirement and having notified my employer, I wanted him to hear from me personally first. I was emotional. Only a few weeks previously he had said to me

"Ray, you have always taught us that if you work in a University, you should be enjoying yourself. Ray, you are not!"

I was shocked at the time but another colleague of the same ilk as Rob, one Rosa Scoble, independently said exactly the same thing to me. Biter bitten, I was being advised with my own advice.

I told Rob late one evening both pieces of news and asked somewhat tearfully if I might continue to do some part-time work in the Department and have some office space. His reply was majestic, something along the lines of:

*"Ray this is **your** Department, without you it would not exist, you made it, you have more right than anyone else to be here. Of course you can continue as much as you like*

whenever you like. And you can keep your office; you will do more with it part-time than anyone else would fulltime."

What a response. But actions speak louder than words. Up until this conversation, Rob was slightly wary of me because he exalted in being Head of Department but worried about having me as his Boss (was I trying to be head as well as dean?) Now the situation had changed and from that moment on, at anytime and anywhere that anyone even hinted at dissatisfaction with me, or disagreed, Rob was on his white horse and rode straight into combat with the individual or people. It was exhilarating to watch!

In between my tenure as Head and Rob's was that of Bob O'Keefe, also a man of distinction like Rob. When Bob was a PhD student at another U.K. university, I had already been a lecturer for 10 years. I must admit, I was not impressed with him (I was more inclined to make judgements of people in those days than I am now!). I believe he found me similarly likeable from his point of view. Bob served his apprenticeship and went to work in a prominent USA University. The next time I saw him was at an international conference in Athens in 1995. He was self-confident and tremendously knowledgeable. He took a European Community bureaucrat to pieces over policy issues with ease and with perfect justification. Jasna asked me who this man was and wasn't he just what I was looking for as a Professor and follow-on Head for my Department. Never mind my legacy views about him, the answer was absolutely yes, and so I went after him. Note here that the view one holds of another person when you first meet can make you blind to talent if you do not mentally update on that person afterwards. I got Bob in early 1996 and became known as the 'man who brought Bob back from America' among his large wider family.

Bob took over from me in 1997 and did many good things, continuing expansion and improving quality. This may sound like more of the same, but it is not easy to follow success with success, and if you do, you do not easily get the credit for what you have achieved. It is very easy to turn inherited success into anything covering a wide range of possibilities: from unrecognised success as good as anything preceding (i.e. Bob); to unmitigated disaster. The University certainly underrated him and on completion as Head he was gratuitously insulted in a variety of ways. But he had expected no more and had secured the job of Head of Surrey's Business School, which he took up in 2000. Bob is now one of only three Deans at Surrey, effectively an Executive Professor. He should be a Vice-Chancellor and maybe he will.

When I started to let everyone know my situation, I wanted Bob to hear it from me, face-to-face. I phoned him and asked him to come to Brunel to see me. When – now? Can't we do it by phone - no? Can you come to Surrey - no. Tomorrow - no.

He halted the meeting he was in and drove over. I told him my news. He was shocked, he was angry, he was upset. He offered to sort someone out for me. He needed time and space, but as he left he thanked me for asking him to come, that he appreciated getting the news directly from me. Later that afternoon he called in on Rob Macredie who was now Head and exchanged outraged comments. But the thing he said to Rob that heartened me was that "Ray is the only person in the world who could call him to come over on the spot without a reason". And he told Rob he was glad I had.

There are many friends who I do not name in this book, not because their reactions were not important to me (they were extremely welcome at the time) but because the reactions were similar to those already described. The reader would find a repetitious listing of such reactions somewhat tedious. These reactions were however very heartening and I treasure them all.

5.4 TELLING COLLEAGUES AND ACQUAINTANCES

So far I have reported pleasant reactions, because after all I have covered friends and relatives. With colleagues, some of whom would be transient friends (i.e. whilst we worked together) the reactions would be much more diverse. For example, one of my PhD students who got her first lecturing post with me at Brunel and was at that time a Senior Lecturer, wrote to me about a diet I should follow and how this would improve my lifestyle! Well meant I am sure, and from her point of view probably sound advice given her personal beliefs. But what did she think I would do with this advice under the circumstances?

Some apologised for having differences with me and hoped they had not brought about either my illness or my decision to retire. Some showed complete indifference, I was retiring, goodbye, no need to talk to you and no need to bother with your views. Some people I had helped, given advice too, and/or assisted with their promotions had been grateful at the time. But with my demise, I was no longer worth paying any attention to since my influence had ceased (they thought). One of my ex-Heads of Department who had flattered me and assumed an air of careful attention to my every view as the Dean suddenly no longer could find the time of day to say hello to me.

Such hypocrisy verging on verbal abuse was a very small percentage of colleagues and says much more about them than about anyone else.

Most reactions were friendly and expressed regret, and came from all over Brunel and everywhere else in the world where people knew me. In my Department I returned to my old office as a God, everybody wanted to help me and commiserate with me and any request I had was treated with reverence. To give the reader a feel for some of this adulation and respect, here are a few quotes from what people wrote to me (so the reader can now jump to the next section if this type of thing is not for you).

5.5 TELLING NEW PEOPLE

When I am up and about, people I meet are unaware I have a health problem. But then, if I was not able to hold my own in public, I would not be in public.

For example, last December I went to a conference in Miami for four days. My attendance was a late booking, because I had not intended to go to this annual conference on this occasion. But then I heard I was going to be awarded a Distinguished Contributions in Simulation Award by a learned society.

Reactions to me coming out

I am sorry to hear of your illness but must say that you have hidden it extremely effectively. ... Many thanks for your support and encouragement.

... From a selfish point of view we will be extremely happy to see more of you in the department ...

Ray's a great guy and has given me a lot of moral support since starting at Brunel.

My admiration of the academic rigour and administrative structures you put in place ... knows almost no bounds ... although I know you didn't manage it single-handed you were the catalyst and leader.

You are one of the most sincere and reliable persons I've met in the academia,

...you have referred to us, your PhD students, as your children. ... you may have not realised how true it is. ... You have been an excellent example of what I want to be in my professional and personal life. ... The best I learned from you, though, is not how to write a PhD but how to look at life from another dimension.

I was sad that your vision and courage would not be directly available to the Faculty or the University.

... your restructuring ... It is innovative, ingenious and above all exciting ... It seems to me that you have grasped – perhaps alone in the university - ...

... how much I'd miss the sense of fun and creativity with which you operate.

... someone else will have to do all the challenging and innovating and pushing back of boundaries and there isn't an obvious candidate.

Take care, mate.

B____r, b____r, b____r ...

I realised that a lot of people had made a lot of effort to get me the award, and so I decided to attend. Searching for flights, I found the lowest price was a hotel/flight combination, and the hotel was only a few miles away from the conference hotel.

I gave the matter careful consideration, made the booking, and then tried to book the conference hotel as well. It was fully booked. But why did I need two hotel rooms? Let me explain what happened and then things will become clearer. After landing in Miami I went to the conference hotel. As I expected, they had rooms available which I could book at the conference rate. So I stayed in a room in the conference hotel. I was tired from the travelling, and participating in a large conference is quite demanding (over 700 delegates). So, not surprisingly, I needed to retreat from the conference at times to my room to allow myself to recuperate. This occurred four times during my four day stay. Now, if I had been staying 10 minutes away in another hotel, choosing to have a break from the conference is more problematic. In order to go back to a room that far away, involving the hire of a taxi, I would have to be sure that it was necessary to make the trip. This could lead to delaying decisions, which might mean I take the taxi back to the hotel later, and be in a much worse physical condition.

Similarly for the return journey. I would have to be reasonably confident that I had recovered before returning. But staying in the conference hotel allowed me to retreat to my room whenever I was in doubt, and return to the conference as soon as I felt able, knowing in both cases that if I was wrong, I could easily retrieve the situation. So, when I was at the conference, I was obviously operating quite well, so how would anyone know there was a health problem? And if I had a health problem, I was in my room and could not be seen. So every new person I met would be surprised if, during the course of a conversation, the issue of my illness came up.

I have not been shy proclaiming my circumstances far and wide since deciding to come out (see next chapter). In the journal I co-edit, many of my editorials covered aspects of my illness. I have mentioned the disease in numerous talks I have given, as well as giving the benefits of my experiences to all and sundry who will listen. One might have thought everyone in the community would have heard. Not so, I meet many experienced professionals engaged in similar activities to mine who have no knowledge about me at all!

When I meet people more formally, I will endeavour to introduce the topic to them ASAP. I am well rewarded in this approach since Jasna or Carole will help keep people at bay until I am ready for them. If the business to be conducted is allowed more than an hour in my diary, then my novice visitor will find themselves engaged in a 'how to improve their life' conversation which leaves them reeling and grateful when they depart. It would be difficult after such a conversation for anyone to forget my state.

Jasna is firmly entrenched in a tennis club, which is not an obsession for her (unlike my activities) and only occupies Tuesdays, Wednesdays and Fridays apart from half the weekend! With local neighbours to add in, we do a comfortable amount of entertaining and being entertained. Before our new friends have got to grips with us, I have been encouraged to do my dancing if necessary in some part of the house or the garden. Most new acquaintances are soon exposed to various aspects of my illness and methods of dealing with it.

5.6 FAMILY NOW

Many years have passed since I told my family, so things have settled down considerably. All members of my family seem always conscious of my condition, and make allowances for it whether needed or not. My father, born in 1920 treats me as if I need care and attention much more than he does! But then his younger wife Pat (by 25 years) has had Multiple Sclerosis for over 10 years now for which she seems unable to fight very vigorously. So my Dad looks after her, and in some ways this keeps him going. My Dad has read much of this book and his comment is that it seems to him to be very accurate. Being the age he is, he comes from a generation with their particular views of life, which includes scepticism of the existence of clinical depression. After Dad read my Chapter Two, I have heard him comment that maybe his wife is unkind to him because she is depressed, and that maybe unfortunately she cannot help herself more. So I like to think some benefit has come from writing the book already. Dad even puts up with my need to go off and dance a bit sometimes. An example of his approach to life is that he is worrying lately about how long he has left because "I still have about 25 years worth of things to do."! A great example to us all.

My brother David, when reading parts of the book, answers that he finds it 'sad' to read the book when I ask him about the quality and content of the writing. This is for me further confirmation that people like David who can appear unemotional at all times to all and sundry can be hiding deep feelings.

All families carry internal disagreements and supposed insults and grievances, but it seems that my being a Parkinson's sufferer absolves me from much of this. So at my 60th birthday party, hosted by my daughter, son-in-law and the 5 year old fabulous twin grandsons, everyone turned up and at my request, told stories about me. Everyone including my ex-wife Marianne, who not only was talking to my wife Jasna amicably earlier (were they exchanging notes about me?!), but also then joined in the story telling. I heard things I had never heard before. In particular I have always thought that since I only became professionally ambitious at the age of 35 that I was also not particularly determined until then. But apparently I was always like this according to a story told by my older brother David at the family gathering – accordingly I offer the story to you the reader entitled as my 60th birthday party revelation vignette.

My 60th Birthday Party Revelation Vignette

I do not remember any of the activity described in my brother David's story of me, but clearly it can be seen to be true by the fact that he has nursed the incidents for over 40 years and only revealed them for the first time at the birthday party. Apparently around our teenage years (David is 3 ½ years older than me) I gave him my view that any game was only worth playing if all players had some chance of winning.

That sounds right to me now as well – what is the point in playing any game if you cannot win at all.

Then David moved further back in history to when we were both pre-teen and played cowboys and Indians together in the local woods – except that we both had toy revolvers (cap guns) so we were both cowboys. The game was to move around the woods and try and shoot (simulated loud noise followed by the claim "you're dead") before your opponent shot you. But such games needed a referee, and clearly age came before beauty (sic) and so David generously called the result which went something like:

I shot him and he declared a miss

He shot me and he declared a hit.

He says I got quite annoyed by this partisanship. Why would I not?

On one occasion I apparently built up steam about the way the game was going until the game suddenly stopped as David called my latest shot a miss yet again, only to find my gun hitting him on the head. In those days guns were not made of plastic but of die-cast metal, lots of it and quite heavy.

David was not dead but I believe his refereeing improved after that and at the birthday party he was able to apply the first part of the story to the second part that preceded it in time. I am glad to hear that my advising of people started out so early in life!

My grandsons make no allowances for me, since for them I am who I am. I must admit I am very careful with them, and do not attempt vigorous physical activity with them – I would never forgive myself if some aspect of my disease caused them injury in such a situation.

Everyone is cautious about my health and cancel meetings if any of them has a cold (which would wipe out my medicine if I caught it).

And I am still giving advice.

There is one exception to all of this, which will either be obvious or a complete surprise. My wife Jasna is still in denial about my condition. I have explained this supposed anomaly in section 4.6 when I covered the subject of Jasna the Carer. In that section I emphasised the different difficulties faced by a Parkinson's sufferer or anyone else who is ill I suspect, and the carer(s).

5.7 PEOPLE AND ME

I often discuss with people my professional position. I seem to be working but I am not an employee. So why am I working? Or why am I not in a job? Or am I not too ill for a part-time honorary job? In the next chapter I explain how my pension did not allow me to take up part-time work in a late change of pension rules which caught me out. But I am 'working': unpaid but that implies no responsibilities; only on what I want to do; only when I want to do it; with job satisfaction otherwise I would not be there; and fulfilling my need to interact with people to challenge, pursue and critique ideas. I am conscious though that my illness is never far away in any conversation, ready to pop up for a variety of reasons:

- As a reason why I cannot take on some activity or other
- As an excuse for not doing something on time
- Casual conversation which usually will include queries about my health – and which I answer!

- Telling war stories, for which my health and how I got here is an endless source of material.
- Using vignettes of my experience to illuminate any advice I may be giving
- To help people help themselves by using my health experience to detect some problems they have and then to compare experiences to reassure.
- And so on.

Do I talk about my illness all the time? Not quite. Do I talk about it too much? Probably. I am too absorbed by it? Probably. Is there evidence of this? Well yes, you are reading this book!

But it is difficult to put it out of mind for long. I take medicine about every two and a half hours which obviously reminds me. And if I forget the medicine, going 'off' reminds me with a vengeance. Needing to dance every now and then is a fairly forceful way of remembering. Sitting uncomfortably, handling paper with difficulty, and many other physical things – all these are constant reminders. As you can imagine, I could be quite boring.

But you the reader can help me – how? Buy this book (many times and give it to friends). Then I can be motivated to write the non-Parkinson's disease autobiographies and then you dear reader can be bored by them in a different way to this book!

CHAPTER 6

WORKING AND RETIREMENT

"Welfare Benefits Benefit ... Welfare" (author)

A healthy individual in full time employment probably feels that life is already too complicated in terms of bureaucracy, the business of form filling, notifying various agencies of change of circumstances etc. Little of this goes away when you retire or are out of work, but a whole host of other agencies enter your life, each requiring their own bureaucratic needs to be satisfied largely for their own sake I believe. This chapter discusses my experiences so far, ranging from the private sector (private health insurance, insurance company based protection plans, motor car insurance) to quasi-governmental agencies (the universities pension scheme) to out-and-out government agencies (state pensions, benefits, disability recognition, and driving licence).

All such bodies or organisations are apparently offering services, although who is serving who can be difficult to determine. I have some views on the natural development of services over time, of which the main is that it is in the nature of any service department to spend an ever increasing proportion of its available time on internal communications as the number of employees in the service department rises. So, with growth, they tend towards increasing ineffectiveness.

I have not been totally efficient in my dealings with all these agencies, and fortunately I am not in such a financial position that I have needed to be. But how the poor cope is beyond me – I suppose needs must. One hears stories of scroungers and the work shy etc, but the impression I get is that whilst agencies advertise for claimants to claim their rights, the processes for doing that are more aligned at making the agency efficient rather than making claiming straight forward.

6.1 PRIVATE HEALTH INSURANCE

As mentioned in the Preface, when I diagnosed myself in December 1999, we did not have any private health care, and we expected the U.K Government's National Health Service (NHS) would take some time before much happened in the way of treatment. This is not meant to be a criticism of the quality of service delivered by the NHS (which I believe is exceptionally good given that the resource demands are severely in excess of the supply), merely an expectation of how resource constrained organisations run more slowly. Fortuitously, Jasna was moving from her previous employer to join the Department of Information and Systems and Computing (DISC) at Brunel University[1]. As an inducement to becoming a member of a private health insurance scheme she was offered a history-free membership for herself and her spouse. We seized the opportunity, what a gift!

But it wasn't. At first all my private health costs were met. Gradually, the benefits were reduced annually until in the end none of my costs were met since my condition was chronic and only emergency treatment qualified for support. Jasna had some physiotherapy sessions to help her with some back problems. From about 10 a year at the start they reduced by around about 2 every year. In no one year did we receive more in benefits than we paid in premiums, not even in the first year, the major year of

---

[1] Jasna's contribution to DISC was already immense in that she was a 'secondary' or 'passive' manager of the Department since I brought all the problems home with me in the early days – a form of secondary or passive managing on a par to the meaning of secondary smoking for smokers

tests and diagnosis for me. And not only do premiums rise with inflation, but also with age. There is a certain irony for me that as you get older the chances of serious illness increases, so the premium rises to cover the increased risk. But that is exactly what an insurance scheme is supposed to deal with, a levelling out of cost amongst a community to cover the unlucky members. Private health insurance effectively shares risk amongst small self contained risk groups where each group is made up of risk-alike members!

We thought about it and decided to stop our membership and carefully bank the premiums in a savings account. After about 6 years the account is very healthy and the costs of private health so far have been less than 20% of the savings. So private health insurance taught us how to make a profit for ourselves. On reflection I observe:

- It served us right for greedily jumping aboard seemingly to our advantage
- A legacy free policy for a husband and wife can only be offered if the premiums cover the unknown risks
- Private health insurance companies are not philanthropic; they are commercial organisations out to make a profit. If they did not, they would go out of business

I would like to offer some thoughts on how private health insurance probably works. We have been taught to manage our money better. In a sense we are a mutual society of two. Of course there is the risk of being cleaned out by a major life threatening illness. Now, if we spread the risks with some friends, pooling our resources, we could reduce the risk, especially as the number of friends grew. But then some would default. Proper accounts would have to be kept. Everyone's tax situation could probably improve if the scheme were run through a charity or something similar. This would have to be properly run, so before long professional managers would be brought on board. They would start to worry about unfairness's among the beneficiaries, and about personal concerns such as incentives, and participatory benefits. Survival of the scheme would require consideration of the need to cover employer risk and measure performance. Performance would probably require financial targets. And from there, it is clear that eventually profit would emerge as a financial target. Oh well, maybe this is the natural order of things?

On reflection I have no regrets. As you can see I learned something!

6.2 MY PENSION SCHEME AND PART-TIME WORKING

I was a member of the University sector's contributory pension scheme all my career (now known as the Universities Superannuation Scheme, or USS for short). The USS benefits that accrue after 40 years service are a pension of around half the salary over the last few years. Retirement due to permanent illness was treated as if you had retired at 65, and the years between early retirement and 65 are made up. So I retired on half salary in 2003 since by the time I was 65 I would have done 41 years service. For many people this might appear to be a generous scheme, but I would like to start this section by investigating the word 'generous'.

Contributors to this pension scheme pay a flat percentage of their salary into the scheme (around 6-7%) and their employer makes a 14-20% contribution (this has varied over the years). Is this generous of employers? I think not, this money like all money comes from University finances, a mixture of government funding, student fees, research grant income and other miscellaneous sources. The money spent on pensions could be spent in other ways. For example, salaries could be that much higher. So the pension scheme is a deferred income scheme whereby one is encouraged to save for the future by forgoing current income. There are tax advantages, as there are for the population at large: academics benefit no more or less than any other professionals.

What of the generosity for sickness retirement? Well that is factored into the contributions and benefits as they are for the pensions themselves. The difference if anything is that since pensions are retail prices indexed, which usually lags behind average wage rises, the pension starts to depreciate against current earners. So in my case for example, retiring 9 years before I am 65 means that when I am 65 my sickness pension will have lagged behind by 20-30%. This is before even considering that with health I would have continued in my job, and with continuing success I would have retired on an even higher pension. So maybe when I am 65 I will be getting 40-60% of what a healthy retirement would have given me. Now please do not get me wrong, I am not complaining, I am merely starting to translate the word generous into practicalities.

The scheme up until the year of my retirement also made provision for sickness retirees to continue to work part-time without loss of benefit as long as the gross income from the pension and employment did not exceed the salary at retirement. This was quite generous since at the maximum, a gross income equal to final salary would give a net income that could be 15-30% higher than previous net income. The reasons for this are that pension and tax contributions would stop or reduce on the pension itself and the tax burden might be lower on the part-time earnings. But this was not the motivation for the changes made to the scheme in 2003. There is one rumour that suggests some universities might have solved the problem of a dissident colleague by seeking a 'medical condition' that enabled early retirement. This rid the University of the Dissident and the financial burden fell upon the pension scheme. Now whether true or not, such thinking would lead to a critical examination of the sickness retirement provision. In any event pressure on the pension funds would also lead to such a critical examination. Whatever the reasons for the review, what emerged is very simple and clear:

If you cannot work and are claiming full pension, then you cannot work. So no part-time working.

If you want to retire because of sickness, but can work part-time, then take a pro rata pension! So half-time working would be supported by a pension of half full entitlement.

This logic is so simple it is irresistible. Is it possible that anything is left out? Well, there is the not insignificant fact that the pension does not hold its relative value against earnings. But ignoring that first let me explain what happened to me and then I shall pose a dilemma.

When I asked for retirement in 2003 I was not aware of any changes being made to the pension conditions. I was offered full sickness pension from 1 August, but I asked for a delay until 1 October partly so I could settle a few matters properly and partly because I had calculated that my pension would benefit significantly from such a delay (it did). The notification of my pension award to the University, copied to me included the following text:

> "We would like to remind you of the circumstances under which ill-health early retirement is granted – and hence the reasons why the ill-health provision is particularly generous. Therefore, inherent in the decision to offer ill-health retirement in this instance is the assumption that the member is unable to work and will not be working in the future."

I suppose I should have noticed the strength of the phrasing, but being unaware of the changes being made I just assumed this was standard 'behave yourself' text. I applied to the pension scheme to be allowed to work part-time. I spoke on the telephone seeking advice, which whilst circumspect, did not warn me of what was to come. The response to my written request was a letter suggesting that my request was going to be put into the hands of the lawyers and would I prepare income and expenditure statements. I was quite upset for reasons I shall now explain.

After my self-diagnosis in December 1999 I continued working, because I loved the job and had never looked forward to normal retirement at 65 let alone 52 as I then was. I lasted three and a half years until summer 2003. I was by then physically run down but more ominously, mentally at the end of my tether. I needed some security in my life, something solid I could depend on. This was the pension's role for me. With half of my salary secured as a pension, then I could work part-time as much as I could handle without risk. Everyone of course would like some security in their lives. But even though the effect on me of Parkinson's disease was not to reduce my abilities or confidence meeting challenges head on, when the challenges came from behind as described later in this chapter, I was in turmoil.

The letter from the pension provider threw me into a state of anxiety. I investigated further and found the changes in pension provision in documents I obtained in November 2003 (ironically from new colleagues in my Department showing me their new employee's pensions literature). It became apparent that these changes were effective from 1 August (the start of the financial year) and that I was being handled on that basis even though I was not aware of the changes being made until after I had retired. You may think I could have made the case that I have made here, but I was not in the right state of mind at that time to do so. The security I had sought and thought I had found was being threatened and my whole world suddenly seemed ready to turn upside down again. I wrote back stating that the letter I had received had caused me anxiety and that I wished to withdraw my application and would be grateful if the matter could now be considered closed. I also said that I was in no position to fulfil any paid employment conditions (reliability and timing are what I had in mind). The reply I got to this letter graciously apologised for my anxiety and agreed to close the matter.

At this point I want the reader to be clear that I am not accusing anyone of misbehaviour, I am not blaming anyone, I understand in particular the responses I got from my pension provider and I do not have any reason to believe it was possible for them to react differently or better. But I would like to make some observations and recommendations that could help people like me if they could in any way be acted on without compromising the agency.

First, since I was retired on grounds of ill health the medical evidence should be considered when looking at each case. All my medical providers had written quite clearly stating that whilst I should take retirement, part-time work would help me cope with my condition more easily. (I have subsequently handled this medical advice through the free provision of my help to both my only employers, Brunel University and the LSE. My reliability and timeliness require great patience).

And then I am a human being. If there was a problem with what I was applying for why not pick up the telephone and have a chat. Or invite me to come and have a chat. Then I would be a human being with needs and problems not a set of rules and regulations applied to a name but not a person.

But pension agencies are not social workers they are fund administrators. True but the funds being administered are the accumulated efforts of its members and with the purpose of helping its members. The pension fund uses the language of trustees and beneficiaries, and things being granted as though I was lucky to receive a pension, rather than getting the benefits from a scheme I am a member of. If the latter were given precedence then maybe I would be a human being with Parkinson's disease to be considered as such.

Just a suggestion.

6.3 INCOME PROTECTION PLAN

Many years ago in 1986 I took out a number of policies with an assurance plc, one of which was an income protection plan. The basic idea behind this plan was to cover that part of my income from outside earnings above my University salary. My University pension covered my University salary, but no more. By picking an indexed premium I would receive benefits related to my non-University income if I had to retire through sickness.

So when I retired, I checked through the policy and my first crude calculations showed a very poor return. During the time from when the policy started, various changes had been made to the policy, including changing the limits on benefit and changing the various formulae for calculating the benefit. These changes did not seem to match my original understanding of the intention of the scheme.

In the course of discussing the policy by telephone, I made this observation about the scheme and the response was slightly aggressive. Was I suggesting something untoward? No, I was merely observing that the scheme did not appear as though it was going to deliver anything like the intended benefits discussed when I took the policy out. The company reacted to my comments by moving into formal procedure mode and I was asked to state my case. I volunteered that since the policy did not seem to match the agreed objectives at the time I took it out, then maybe we should agree to that and that all my premiums should be returned.

The company considered my proposition for some time and then wrote me a long adjudication letter basically telling me that I had been kept informed of all policy changes as they occurred, and that I could have asked for a review at any time but I had not and so:

> *"In the circumstances I regret your request for a return of the contributions you have been paid has been rejected.*
>
> *This is our final outcome letter and should you be dissatisfied with the outcome of our investigation you can refer your complaint to the Financial Ombudsman Service ... "*

Investigation, conclusions drawn and sentence all delivered by the company. But fortunately when the income protection plan calculations were made on accurate data, it turned out that whilst the benefit was nothing like the potential maximum, it was larger than I had first anticipated and would accumulate to easily much more than a repayment of the premiums would have achieved.

However, it pays to check these things very carefully. As will be discussed in the next section I did not get round to applying for any state benefits until late 2008 after the income protection benefits had ceased on my 60th birthday. I applied for incapacity benefit which was granted but my benefit was £0 since my pension is too high. The assurance company benefits were calculated as follows: first calculate the total income I should receive according to the policy and then my University pension was subtracted from that; and then the State Incapacity Benefit at the maximum rate was subtracted from the remainder. But far from receiving the State Incapacity Benefit at the maximum rate, because the benefit is means tested, I have never been entitled to receive any money.

When I first claimed from the company in 2003, I spoke to my insurance agent who had inherited my portfolio from the agent who sold me all the company's policies in the first place. The agent paid me a visit and from then onwards, the company had been civilised and friendly with my applications.

So when I realised what had happened with my income protection plan with respect to incapacity benefit, I contacted the agent again and he asked me to write a letter explaining the situation either to him or to the company and to claim the unpaid equivalent of these monies for the duration of the benefits paid. I sent the letter to the agent, remembering how his previous personal intervention had made my life so much easier. A few weeks later, the company sent me a letter saying that they agreed with my calculations and I have now received the money.

So who is this agent? He is one of the most honest and pleasant people I have ever dealt with. I can forward emails to him, for which an email address is given in the acknowledgements at the end of the book. Since the world is not overstocked with conscientious, trust worthy competent individuals, I feel duty bound to inform as many people as I can of this man's talents.

The income benefits I have received have come monthly by cheque. When I suggested it would be more convenient to have it paid directly into my bank account I was told that this could not be done. But I have always paid my premiums by direct debit and it would be cheaper to pay me this way rather than send a cheque. So why this petty decision?

My guess is that claimants are looked upon first as a danger to profits and secondly as potentially dishonest. So my benefits were paid by cheque so that the deposit went into my account and therefore I had not deceased. Nearly all my dealings with the company have been greatly improved my independent financial advisor has been involved. What a difference a man of integrity, honesty and professionalism can make!

6.4 Welfare Benefits Benefit ... Welfare

In chapter 2 I discussed my experiences with mental health and made a plea for openness. Later in this chapter I discuss illness and work, and suggest that illness and a job are not necessarily incompatible and society might like to consider this. Now I wish to make some suggestions about welfare systems.

Welfare systems provide a service to its 'customers', which is why I started the chapter with my observations about how as a service organisation grows, disproportionally more time is given over to internal matters until the time left for 'customers' then starts to decrease in absolute terms as the service organisation keeps expanding until eventually no service is provided at all. The service organisation has a life of its own, which has nothing to do with the rest of the world.

And what of the 'customer' or 'consumer'? Well, they are a bit of a nuisance. It would not be so bad if they would find out how the service organisation works (reading brochures, guides, using the web etc) and then restricted their needs to exactly what was allowed. After all you cannot expect a welfare system to be considering how the interaction looks like from the customer point of view.

So if we look back on this chapter, private health insurance is a misleading name for what is essentially an emergency health only insurance provision. The pension scheme looks fair on paper but without any human input, its mechanistic approach does not worry about anything but the basics, and excludes pensioners as human beings. The income protection plan in the end delivered a product that had been amended over time, and if it is not what you remember signing up to and you have not kept up to date with the changes, that is entirely your own fault.

State benefits might be understood by a healthy civil servant or politician whose area of professional expertise this is, but to expect the socially disadvantaged or the sick etc to make much sense of the system rather loses sight by the professionals as to why such people are in need in the first place.

The disabled car sticker (section 3.5) and three year driver's licences (section 3.6) are not organised around the sensitivities of the sick and disabled people who have to use these systems. Rule following is safe, and if there is no rule, it cannot be done.

So, it is time to rethink welfare benefits. Back to basics, what is the need or right and then how can it effectively be delivered. Welfare providers need to train their staff on what it is like to be in the position of someone needing welfare support. Maybe they should be managed somehow by the welfare 'needsters' rather than by those who have no need.

Every part of the professional support system I have encountered as a Parkinson's sufferer assumes that full-health is normality, and that a sick person is abnormal. So the welfare beneficiary is 'lucky' to be granted what is effectively their earned right; or the beneficiary should be grateful for the special procedures introduced to deal with him/her, even though the procedures do not attempt to cater for the needs of the beneficiary. That is because the procedures are for the convenience of administering the welfare system, and not its delivery effectiveness. I am not sure what training people who operate the above systems get, so maybe the following suggestion is already happening. I take the idea from the treatment of speeding offenders, who are sometimes offered a training course about speeding as an alternative to a fine or worse. I have heard many times that the training course, showing scenes of accidents, and injured people recovering as a result, has had a great effect on the speeding offender. In a similar vein, my car once broke down in the middle of some road works. Until then I had often thought that the speed limits through road works were sometimes a bit low. But broken down, waiting for rescue, was a scary business, as vehicles appeared to be hurling themselves in your direction, ready to make a last minute avoiding action - we all hoped!

Films about life showing the complaints that welfare seekers have about the welfare systems could be used to train welfare staff so that they can distinguish between awkward behaviour and behaviour that is of necessity awkward. Similarly for other aspects of being a welfare worker. Just a thought.

6.5 RETIREMENT – SHOULD I STAY OR SHOULD I GO?

The story of my continuing in work and then my retirement was outlined in section 1.5. A full description of the politics involved is only relevant to this book where it relates to Parkinson's disease. The full story is one of conspiracy, skulduggery, stabbing in the back etc. For those readers who are disappointed not to read this story in this book, the forthcoming autobiography *Lucky Ray* (see The Seven Book Autobiography appendix) will reveal all (subject to legal constraints). In the remaining three sections of this chapter, the major determinant of financial well-being is considered, that is job income or retirement. These matters are considered in general terms using my simplified case as an example where appropriate.

There are a number of decisions that someone who is seriously ill may be in a position to decide to make, of which two of the most fundamental ones might be: when to, and who to, tell you are ill; and a third might be when to retire if this is not immediately determined by the illness. To some extent these questions are interlinked, and the decisions might be adjusted in their timings by the activities of others, and we shall see that this is what happened to me. Rather than present what would be a rather dull chronology, which would not of course be replicated in anything like its entirety by another Parkinson's sufferer, I have decided to present these critical decisions in this and the following section. This particular method of presentation might assist any reader who has to take similar decisions. The reader might benefit from my experiences, not of course by imitation but as a basis for thinking about them. However in my story, the content of these sections ran in parallel – I shall therefore try and indicate the major overlaps where I remember to do so.

The next section following this one deals with the question of the public declaration of your medical condition and then in my case the effect on everyone when I did go public.

I have never contemplated retirement with anything other than great distaste. I love my job, so much so that even in retirement I am doing as much of it as I can still on a non-salaried basis for both my previous employers (admittedly the most pleasurable parts). We saw in section 6.2 above why it is difficult for me to be paid, which turns out to be a Catch 22 situation for me. But the main point to reiterate is: I did not want to retire from the moment I diagnosed myself with Parkinson's disease in December 1999 until, only under intense pressure, I gave way in the summer of 2003.

So this section is largely concerned with my fight to keep going, to not only keep and do my job, but to do it exceptionally well. I like to think I had done this with increasing effectiveness since becoming ambitious in Rio de Janeiro in 1982. But now I was aware that the better I performed, the longer I would keep my job. And if I performed well but still had to retire early then my pension would be appropriately commensurate. I consciously pursued this policy of performing well to keep my job. I rise to challenges in life. I do not like to give in to something I do not want to do or I think is wrong. I fear that giving in for me is the start of the downward path to giving in full-stop. I still believe that. That is one of the reasons for writing this book.

Let me reveal some of the thinking I went through in those first anxious months of my first year of treatment in 2000. I drew up a table of alternative courses of action, recreated in Table 7 below. I could retire (working part time or not), with the obvious positive, negative and neutral outcomes. Similarly for the choice of staying in the job. I could also break free from this potentially limited way of thinking which is usually expressed in terms of just two stark choices. "Two stark choice" decisions lead you to make the least bad choice, which is not necessarily a pleasant state to be in. Opening up potential alternatives, either by developing some previous thinking, or by coming up with entirely new alternatives by 'thinking outside the box', are ways of making choice palatable rather than just least unpleasant.

I came up with 'Books to write' and 'Ideas to develop' as possible ways forward for me. I have already quoted Woody Allen's sentiment "I don't want to be immortal because of the words I wrote, I want to be immortal because I didn't die". However, since the latter is not an option, I would like to see if I can achieve some fulfilment from the former part.

Table 7. Alternative Courses of Action and Possible Outcome States

Actions	Outcome States
Retire	Neutral
	Positive
	Negative
Full time working	Neutral
	Positive
	Negative
Books to write	?
Ideas to develop	?

So looking at each action in Table 7 in turn, the following list shows some of the major components of a decision to retire.

Outcomes of Retiring

Positive:

- Work part-time to make up salary loss (which was not allowed when I actually did retire – see 6.2)
- Private insurance income would be topped-up until 60, (and endowment free).
- The lump sum can be used to reduce the mortgage, and hence monthly payments; possibly buy property in Croatia to make life more comfortable and reduce future holiday costs. Property would at least hold its value.
- Write books and make money (?)
- Consultancy to earn more money (again, which was not allowed when I actually did retire – see 6.2)

Neutral:

- Pension half salary
- 150% lump sum

Negative:

- Part-time work is insecure: if there is a small financial crisis, then it is goodbye to part-timers
- Extra income gained by leveraging full-time post lost
- Pension increases by retail price index, which is usually less than the average wage/salary increase
- And with promotion, over 10 years, the pension could be half of what it would have been by retiring at age 65
- Be nobody!
- No people contact. Inactivity turns into depression again?

The next list shows some of the major components of a decision to stay in full time employment. Again, it turns out that some of the assumptions made in these tables are wrong. Getting a top research rating for the Department is no longer meaningful since research power is now measured in terms of ratings times the number of people submitted. Nor is it moving the University towards the top 20 Universities.

Outcomes of Continuing in Full-Time Employment
Positive:

- Larger pension
- Pro-Vice Chancellor or even Vice Chancellor
- Help Department achieve a top research rating
- Help University move towards the top 20 universities
- Continue being a 'Demi-God'
- Help people

- Jasna would be happier

Neutral:
- Salary increases

Negative:
- Over worked
- Insurance company pension top up lost
- If pushed out of job later, pension would not be full pension

The next list shows the intentions in 2000 concerning possible deliverables for the two alternative actions considered at that time. They illustrate perfectly Eisenhower's quote from around D-Day in the Second World War:

"In preparing for battle I have always found that plans are useless, but planning is indispensable."

The section near the end of this book on The Seven Book Autobiography that I now believe I could write, were only conceived of as two books in 2000. This Parkinson's disease book was not conceived of until 2003 for example.

Alternative Actions and Their Outcomes
Books to write:
- Simulation textbook
- Information Systems edited research book
- How I supervise my PhD students
- Paul's Laws

Ideas to develop
- Information systems development

- Simulation research book on building models by web search

But the purpose of showing my work sheets from 2000 is not to show that I got it right or wrong, but to show how I reassured myself at the time that any option could be made to work in certain ways or not, having identified the possibilities. So I could make a choice knowing how to get out of the choice if it did not work. I can only recommend some such formal analysis to help in the darkness that seems to envelop you in the first months or year or two after diagnosis. The analysis does not make a decision for you, but the process of looking at all possibilities and outcomes can provide increased confidence for the decision actually taken.

I decided to continue working and to tell no one about my illness.

I have already explained several times that my skills with people are far superior to my skills handling paper. I asked my consultant Dr Bain if my skill with people and lack of skill with paper was due to Parkinson's disease. *"No, it's your natural inclination exaggerated by Parkinson's disease"* he immediately shot back.

So, I took my illness as an excuse to myself to offload the paperwork side as much as possible, and concentrate on the face to face work. One of the consequences of my body-rattling medication was an improved concentration and memory (I have a useful armoury of quotes stored in my head). My enhanced memory was also useful in avoiding the need to keep notes, which given my writing and typing difficulties, would have distracted me from giving my visitor my full attention. And, it is worth adding, if you deal honestly with everyone, there isn't much you have to remember!

Thus the paperwork that did arrive on my desk would be moved around by me until one of my staff could stand it no longer, would throw away the out of date and trivial, and try and get draft responses for the rest. By and large, I maintained an air of command efficiency and effectiveness that were even reaffirmed after my retirement by the comparative situation that arose.

6.6 COME OUT OR STAY IN?

Should I declare my illness or keep it too myself was a recurring question for me for over three years. In some ways I felt my employer should know of circumstances that might affect my work performance, but I was suspicious of what would happen if I did. In due course I found to some extent that my suspicions were justified. Within six months of informing my employer I had Parkinson's disease I was retired on a full sickness pension due to permanent ill health. And yet until I declared my state of health, no one knew I was ill. Some people retrospectively thought I had been looking tired quite often, but I usually felt the same about them. And I did check my terms and conditions of employment and nowhere did it say I had to make a declaration, a fact confirmed by the appropriate university administrator when I did decide to seek sickness retirement.

What were the advantages and disadvantages of letting people know? At the time of my self-diagnosis I had been in post as Dean of the Faculty of Science for 4 months since September 1999, with five university departments and some research centres under my management, one of six Faculties in the University. I was at one level below the University's Management Group which at that time was made up of the Vice Chancellor, his Deputy the Vice Principal, three Pro Vice Chancellors and several senior administrators. So I was in a position of responsibility and trust both to the employees and students of my Faculty, but also for the well-being of these members of the Faculty to the Vice Chancellor, sometimes through his Senior Management Group. To start to explain why I did not tell the University of my illness I shall quote Oscar Wilde:

"In unimportant matters, style is more important than substance. In important matters style is more important than substance."

I felt that my long term existence as an academic manager would be under threat one way or the other if my illness was public knowledge. Let me conjure up some scenarios for you:

Within the Faculty

Any disappointments would be blamed on my lack of ability because 'I was ill'. Hints would be varyingly made about whether it would be fairer on colleagues if I were to make way for someone who was fit and healthy. My heads of departments would go behind my back to members of Senior Management if they felt I had not represented them effectively 'because I was ill'. I would not understand the complexity of the case I was being presented with if I did not give it the desired support because 'I was ill'. Of course I could avoid this problem if I kept everyone happy all of the time. This is impossible unless the world is to stand still and nothing changes.

At the University management level

Any problem in the Faculty, any disagreeing over policy and was it 'because I was ill'? This would be more pronounced in my case since, as already set out in the preceding chapters, I am very much the sort of person who argues his case relentlessly if I think I am right until either I get my own way or I am persuaded I am wrong (sometimes the latter, but not often). This determination gave me the reputation of being difficult to argue with, which had the tremendous advantage that if people thought I was going to take a position on an issue they would often back down since they did not want to waste their time losing an argument to me. But 'if I was ill' then I would be the messenger to be shot and the message could be ignored because the message was delivered by a sick messenger.

Winning or losing

Of course I would often win the point or carry the day regardless, but then it would be that this was the case because people did not want to upset me 'because I was ill'. An accumulation of such supposed concessions would build up into a cry that this is not fair, everyone having to give way all the time 'because I am ill'.

Cause and effect

I would be aware that because everyone would know that I was ill, I could not be sure whether what I was being told was: either what I should be hearing; or what people thought would be palatable to a sick person. Remember, ordinarily I would already be trying to work out the integrity or otherwise of what I was hearing, the stance my discussant was taking, motivation, rewards, etc. I did not need the management challenge of this extra dimension.

Performance measurements

I would not be able to judge my performance either, was I more successful or otherwise than I would have been if no one knew? I already had the problem of working out for myself if I could recognise the effect on my performance for myself when only I knew. I did not need the challenge of this extra dimension.

Consequences of secrecy

If I made a mess of the job, then it was discovered I had been ill, then not only would I have made a mess but I would be guilty of not adequate warning that my performance might be lower 'because I was ill'. I might collapse in some way and people had the right to know that this could happen.

Well, so much for speculation. After just over three years I announced my illness and within six months I was retired. Cause and effect? Let us just say that the reason for announcing my illness was to determine whether senior management would support me in my ambitions for the Faculty, or whether the pressure to step down would increase (the latter more or less meaning retirement). Six months!

6.7 COULD I WORK NOW?

So far I have handled having Parkinson's disease quite well from what people tell me, what I read, and most importantly what my medical professionals tell me. This leads to a source of puzzlement for many people, who observe my appearance, observe my free work contributions and confuse the two with the question "Why aren't you working?"

If we go back to 2003 I took sickness retirement as late as possible, when I felt I could no longer do my job properly. I had taken myself to what I thought was the limit. Some evidence of this is provided by the almost universal comments I receive about how much better I am looking. People who see me intermittently are very surprised at how much better is the shape I appear to be in compared to a year to three years ago. The fact that when people say this I often do not feel anything like 100%, is I think a measure of how much damage continuing to work on for a further three and a half more years had done to me.

A summary of my job abilities might be captured in an advert for a job that read:

"Wanted. Talented experienced individual, good with people and problem solving, to turn up to work occasionally, by appointment preferably. However it is not a requirement of the job that you keep your appointments, in fact nor that you actually turn up to work at all on a planned visit day. You will not have to account for your activities, nor will you have to do anything you do not want to do. We expect you to offer advice to all and sundry, and to speak your mind openly no matter how difficult that makes the job of our managers. Applicants should seriously consider their

mental state if they believe this advert is genuine."

But this is what I do, and from my point of view it is ideal, I am the unpaid professional. I have just completed my sixth year of unpaid work since retirement, and I am grateful for the patience of my colleagues. I anticipate however that this could be my final year.

We are born and we die. In between one might consider oneself to be healthy, until at some point in time illnesses start to dominate ending in terminal domination. That is one way of looking at it.

Another is to assume that since from the moment we are born, death is inevitable, and illness will catch up with us sooner or later. So then death and illness are the natural states. That makes the time one is healthy a temporary state which has unknown length but certainty of ending. So, if we assume all employees are ill, but some are temporarily healthy, we might then be in a position to offer jobs on this basis. And then maybe I could work.

Otherwise, no I cannot hold down a job.

CHAPTER 7

DANCING FOR LIFE WITH PARKINSON'S DISEASE

When I started writing this book, dancing was already part of my life as a Parkinson's sufferer, but has become so increasingly important to me that the subject warrants its own chapter. Since dancing is a form of exercise, the chapter starts from that perspective, the issue of health. What dancing does for me in general and sometimes as treatment is covered next?

Some 'social' aspects are discussed in the latter sections of the book, such as dancing with an iPod so that the music does not distract others. But this means I am bouncing around wildly for no reason from the viewer's perspective. Such strange behaviour can lead to unfriendly reactions. It does seem that when humans observe 'strange' behaviour, they would rather judge the behaviour than investigate the cause.

The chapter ends with yet another call to society, this time my advocacy of dancing for all. More dancing would generate more happiness, fitness and allow me more freedom of action.

7.1 HEALTH, FITNESS AND RATS

Recent research indicates that Parkinson's sufferers would benefit from exercise in terms: of dealing with their affliction on a day to day basis; and possibly in slowing down the loss of cells in the brain which are the cause of Parkinson's disease. These results I do not find surprising since everyone's health in general could potentially benefit from regular exercise, in the same way that a balanced diet of healthy food consumed in moderation could also maintain or improve one's state of health. These results, if not immediately obvious, become blindingly obvious if you reverse them: eating an unbalanced diet of unhealthy junk food in quantities based on greed rather than need will not improve your health and in the long run will damage your health; lack of exercise will cause your body to be less able to carry out its motor functions and eventually make it difficult to be independently mobile at all.

But Parkinson's sufferers are already not fit or healthy, are they not? The intake of medicine makes the effect of food and drink consumption less predictable. True, but these are debates about directions and not detail. One could hardly expect that if food from fast food shops is a major part of your diet that your body will not deteriorate as for any non-sufferer. Similarly little or no exercise for a Parkinson's sufferer is hardly likely to be of any benefit and just as likely to cause other health problems as it does for non-sufferers (except perhaps for the issue of being able to balance).

If Parkinson's sufferers have difficulty with balance, then exercise might prove difficult, and there may be many forms of exercise that could be harmful. For example, swimming is widely recommended as an excellent form of exercise since it allows muscle development and toning combined with a less strenuous imposition on the body in general because the water can be used to float the frequent stresses away. I have 'tried' swimming without any personal success, as was discussed in chapter one, section three.

The health research tests on the benefits of exercise predominantly relate to running as the exercise of study. I personally finding running far too boring. I do exercise on a semi-recumbent exercise bike at home, which I can tolerate because I can use music as part of the exercise. The reason I do this particular exercise is because of a side-effect of one of my medications, a side effect called Red Leg Syndrome. There is an explanatory vignette called "The Red Leg Syndrome" for readers who like these diversions. But as I have said throughout the book, dancing is my main exercise activity, so much so that I have devoted this whole chapter to it, since I believe that dancing may be of great benefit to other Parkinson's sufferers, and indeed for everyone in general. But how do it compare with other forms of exercise?

I asked this question of a newly appointed Director of a Parkinson's disease Research Centre after he gave a research seminar in which he extolled the virtues of exercise such as running. He thought carefully and said he could see no reason why it should not be of equivalent benefit, but it would be difficult to prove one way or another. Puzzled I enquired why and he replied "... because we cannot teach rats to dance!"

If this answer is not obvious, let me continue by the story my consultant Dr Bain told me.

The Red Leg Syndrome Vignette

One of my medicines from the very beginning of my treatment, Pergolide, probably caused my onset of Red Leg Syndrome after a few years of treatment. Red Leg Syndrome as I understand it, apart from making the lower legs bright red, leaves the skin in relatively poor condition, easy to damage it and pick up an infection. When reports of the side effects of this medicine's usage in the United States hinted at thrombosis effects too, I was despatched to a Deep Vein Thrombosis Clinic to check out the pair of side effects.

On arrival at the Clinic I was asked 'heart or legs' and when replying legs, was dismissively sent to wait over the far side whilst the Clinic got on with the really important patients, the hearts. After 2 hours I, as a leg, was allowed in to a small partitioned area where a clinic doctor who I guess had been on duty for 48 or more hours and a trainee doctor enacted a pantomime for an hour.

The clinic doctor would come in, look totally confused, scratch his head, and then go off in search of some paper form he needed. For 10 minutes the young female trainee doctor and I would make small talk until our doctor returned and the cycle repeated. After the third or fourth such cycle our doctor returned with the Registrar, the top man in the Clinic.

The Registrar quizzed his doctor without reward, looked at the paperwork, looked at my legs and showed clearly he was very unimpressed. "Who sent you here?" he asked of me pointedly, and after explaining the above he said "You tell your neurologist to stick to neurology ....!"

He then proceeded to tell me that the problems I had with my legs were due to lack of exercise.

> This meant my small muscles and capillaries were not clearing the debris in my legs leaving the coloration and deterioration.
>
> Exercise regularly on a machine where your feet are above you heart if possible, or as high relatively as possible. With that Ray the second-class red leg was dismissed for ever from the serious Deep Vein Thrombosis Clinic.
>
> And the Registrar was right. Regular exercise on my semi-recumbent bike and the legs improve accordingly!

In reply to my telling him of the above interchange, he told said that apparently a test carried out on two similar groups of rats involved treating them all by whatever method is used to induce Parkinson's disease type symptoms in rats, and then exercising one group fairly vigorously, and leaving the other group to their own devices. Apparently none of the first group ended up with Parkinson's disease symptoms, and the entire second group did. This may not appear conclusive to some readers, but it is good enough for me when set against the general comments I have made in this introductory section.

One aside on fitness and exercise that shows that life can continue. Since being a university student well over 30 years ago, I have an interest in playing what is called 'Table Football'. This is usually played by two players on each side who control two rods each with a number of figures on each rod that are capable of hitting a ball. The object is to get the ball in the opposing side's goal. I have such a machine at home, on a table which is waist height with eight rods sticking out on each side, wide enough for two people to have control of two rods. Jasna tells me this does not look too attractive in our living room! In spite of Parkinson's disease I am a reasonably good player. Most of the action is in arm movement, in particular wrist spin. Unless I am 'off' I can play a very fast game, especially with fast music being played. People are surprised at my ability, especially if I play in a public place. Young men are not enthusiastic about being challenged and beaten by a man of my age! But it is also good exercise.

And so let us dance on. The titles of the remaining sections of this chapter are largely self-explanatory, except perhaps for 7.3 which concerns the state a Parkinson's sufferer sometimes reverts to when the medicine is not quite working, which my consultant calls going or being 'off' and how I can sometimes use dancing to get back again.

7.2 WHAT DANCING DOES FOR ME

First, I enjoy dancing and more or less always have since I started around the age of 18 (I was too self conscious and introverted before). I have never been particularly elegant, and probably watching me dance might be comparable to watching motorway or freeway traffic pass under an unlit bridge at night (energetic but not entertaining). After becoming a parent, dancing was rare since as we all know, adults don't do that sort of thing except in formally labelled events such as wedding receptions etc (why not?).

When I knew I had Parkinson's disease, at some point in time (but I do not remember exactly when) I found music helpful both walking (music gives my legs something to pace my stride with and thereby gives a regularity to walking and reduces stumbling). And then after a lot of jigging about I discovered not only could I dance, but if I danced fast enough I could move my body so well that it felt as though I had 100% pre-Parkinson's disease control over it again. What a great feeling, something you can only properly appreciate when you have lost it, as I guess is true for any malady. From then onwards dancing has turned into an obsession for me as the rest of this chapter will demonstrate.

When my passion became quite developed I told my consultant Dr Bain who informed me that a recent research result had shown that people who danced were less likely to suffer from senile dementia. Given my low regard for statistics in action, I wonder if this is just the same as the assertion "people who are less likely to suffer from senile dementia are more likely to dance". In any case whilst interesting, it is not particularly useful since if you dance this does not imply you will not get senile dementia nor if you do not dance that you will. Again I suspect that the fitter you are the healthier you are and so the more capable you are of fighting wear and tear and illness.

Given that Parkinson's disease is about movement difficulties when dealing with slow intricate moves, it is not surprising that dancing is more effective the faster it is. And it cannot in my experience be based on any dancing routines or dance styles, because the requirement to be in step with others is not Parkinson's disease movement ability. I dance completely free form to generally fast music (until at last I am kick-started by the dancing) in plenty of space. Space is important because I need to know that my dance steps can be giant leaps for mankind (i.e. me). On one ski holiday disco one of the people I was with decided on several occasions to stand right in front of where I was dancing. Each time, unwillingly because I was enjoying myself, I came to a dead halt. I had experienced this before in non-dancing situations. Once in a restaurant I went to collect my coat from the general racks of coats and as I started looking for my coat, a table of 5 to 6 people finished their visit and joined me coat hunting completely surrounding me. They must have wondered what I was doing standing motionless in the midst of them making no attempt to get my coat and hindering them from getting theirs.

But I do like dancing with a dance partner even though we will not coordinate. A dance partner is a form of undeclared support. If my partner dances reasonably fast this provides me with the encouragement to dance harder/faster/with loose dancing interchange (moving around each other or just missing as the music takes hold). Sometimes a partner will fall in with my variation of dancing and with varying success it can sometimes look highly coordinated. And when, after really getting going and body control returns I can even dance to quite slow songs.

In my garden at home I have a reasonable sized lawn and when I am really moving, I cover large areas in fast paced sweeping turning movements, lots of arm waving, mixtures of delicate and large dancing steps and I am in my personal heaven on earth for a short while. Classical or pop, each can be found delivering me to this state. And though as we shall see next it can sometimes be frustrating, and my dancing activities scarcely meet with universal approval, I wouldn't give it up for almost anything (and I do not know what the 'anything' might be!).

And of course dancing can be extremely helpful when I get a mood swing and whilst this is not me being depressed in the true sense of the word as I explained in Chapter 2, it can still be low enough to make any productive activity not seem worthwhile, and there is always a danger that if not dealt with, then for all I know, the lows could progressively sink lower and lower and … Well, I cannot contemplate that happening again, so 'be not idle' being the main lesson, dancing certainly fulfils that requirement. Half an hour of fast movement usually resuscitates my spirits. It can take a lot longer if I am 'off' as well, but fortunately lows tend to come in the mornings. This means I am usually strong enough to dance myself into the pace required for takeoff and then a further 30 minutes will usually solve both problems.

7.3 GOING 'OFF' AND DANCING ON

Occasionally I go 'off', an expression meaning that my medication is not working adequately or almost not at all. An example of the latter is when I catch the common cold when it seems that the body's defence mechanism attacks the Parkinson's disease medication quite effectively. On one occasion I could only move properly for 2 hours three times a day. Fortunately such events are quite rare and just have to be put up with.

Much more frequently are off periods where it seems the medication last taken does not carry through to the next dose. This could be because the medication needs updating because the need generally is greater, or because I have not taken the medicine on time, or because I have had less sleep than I need, or for some other good reason I am unaware of. Then I can wait for the medicine to kick in or I can – dance!

Trial and error experimentation suggests to me that I can over-ride Parkinson's disease or advance the benefits of the incoming medication if I can dance past a certain speed after which the speed of movement if maintained for a few songs will then mean normal movement for a while. This is not scientific experimentation so I cannot be sure whether dancing has caused the off to go away, or whether the elapsed time has done it. But I do have evidence of some effect as we shall see.

The trick seems to be to get the dancing going at a speed at which I am guessing Parkinson's disease does not affect me. That is, Parkinson's disease stops me doing slow delicate things, but not fast things if I can cross a certain slow/fast customs post between the two states. Once I am safely in fast country, the slower stuff falls into line. There is one not insignificant barrier. The speed required is very high and I am trying to reach it from an almost still state. This can be such a gap that it can take 30 to 60 minutes to get there and since the effort involved over such a time period is very great, exhaustion can set in and then failure. I do not like failure and try to resist giving in.

So what do I do? I go through my iPod playlists looking for suitable tracks. I use mood to guide my selection. Sometimes success comes from a series of quite fast tracks.

I just got going vignette

I am sitting in the garden at Villa Giardino in Bol (see acknowledgements for details about this wonderful hotel) which I entered from my room 30 minutes ago to resume writing this book.

But I was 'off' and I could scarcely move. Now at the best of times I am a two-fingered typist who types in words with an average spelling error of 2 to 3 per word, and when I am 'off' I am liable to delete more good material than I insert.

So, on goes the iPod and off come the shoes. I 'started' with one of my new favourites: Mass Destruction by Faithless from their album Forever Faithless: The Greatest Hits.

This is quite a fast number but too fast to break my rigidity I moved onto two tracks by The Arcade Fire but abandoned both just before their completion because although I was on and off a bit, progress was still too slow. Should I move to very fast or slow? I decided on this occasion very fast since it was late morning and I should have the stamina for it. So Showbiz then Hysteria both by Muse.

I was moving. Whilst seeking the next song, the iPod carried onto the next Muse song Supermassive Black Hole which I continued with because it seemed to match my mood. Now I was moving! I moved to a recent discovery of mine, a 9min. 25 sec. track from Patti Smith called Land from the album Horses from the 1980s

This was excellent reinforcement for the movement I had now attained, with a variety of moods and speeds fast to very slow which enables me to see if movement is temporary still. If all variations are danced to my satisfaction then my movement is probably permanent – for a while!

> I tried a cooling down number, Patti Smith's 2007 cover of Nirvana's Smells Like Teen Spirit from her new album Twelve, but it was hardly cooling.
>
> So, fully mobile again I have just written the text leading into the vignettes and the vignette itself.
>
> In just under half an hour 400 words completed even if I am in a slightly sweaty damp state and spelling errors are 2 to 3 per minute!

If not, 2 extremes are then tried: slow tunes that heat up (or wind-up tunes as I call them), which carry me through the barrier; and super fast tunes that throw me over the barrier suddenly. An example of what I mean is given in the 'I just got going' vignette.

Whichever approach I am taking, the effect visually is of a pathetic older man trying to be iPod trendy but making himself look stupid by shaking, rattling and rolling on and off with attempts at dance steps or even a series of fast steps and then periods of tightly coiled inaction waiting for the body to signal ready to launch torpedo Ray again. A brave friend sat through the whole process and I tell the story in the Christine, the Mendula and Dancing Vignette. In the struggle to get going, I find it easier to use backward movements (which as for ice and roller skating appear easier to do than forward movements) and spins (dancing by turning on the spot or over a metre or two). If forward steps become easy and natural I know I am near take-off.

Why am I confident that it is dancing that overcomes the Parkinson's disease and not the medicine taking effect? Often at the end of the day I would like to relax with some dancing.

Christine, the Mendula and Dancing Vignette

Whilst on my visit to Villa Giardino in late September 2007, I went to dinner with the owner Christine Gratelli to a nearby restaurant the Mendula. The Mendula is run by a man called Pero, a soft friendly individual who had already been persuaded to use his car to take me back to Villa Giardino every time I went to the Mendula alone. The Mendula is basically two terraces on the front of some houses, with some protection over most of the area and some fixtures to make an inside room at one end. The terraces are split level with adjoining staircases. Although it's a bit like eating in someone's front garden, the Mendula in season is very popular because it serves well prepared good food at very reasonable prices.

It was six months to the day that Christine's husband Vinko had died and I had earlier gone to the cemetery with Christine. So it was a dinner conversation about memories, and we were sitting on the non-enclosed terrace when I realised I was late with my medication. As the meal progressed my movements deteriorated, as it happens in parallel with the very few customers on our terrace all finishing their meals and leaving. I had to stop eating because I could hardly use the cutlery so frozen had my body become. I told Christine that I had to stand up and she suggested I dance – the terrace was empty she pointed out.

So in the middle of the terrace I stood barely moving, iPod strapped on and Pero wondering what on earth was going on.

Christine, a respected and forceful woman, explained the situation to Pero leaving him bemused: I was doing no harm and there were no customers although those on the second terrace could see me.

It was a long slow business. At first I barely moved at all. Then gradually occasional collections of steps were forming between longer bouts of inactivity. Then some broken dancing developed half flow and half forced movement. Christine sat patiently observing but not watching intently. Pero occasionally popped a surprised head up the stairs, looked here and there, saw Christine's face and retreated again. At last the opportunity to breakthrough occurred when I found that with one track I was playing I could force myself to keep up with the music, and the forced speed of movement suddenly turned into natural flowing dance movement. I had broken through. A couple of fast tracks to ensure the freedom of movement was maintained when I stopped, and I effortlessly covered the whole terrace in fast flowing steps, spins and other movements. Pero looked even more surprised. When I stopped Christine expressed amazement at the transformation and said she would never have believed it if she had not seen it with her own eyes. How could I be so immobile for so long, and then suddenly so naturally loose and flowing and at speed, with all body parts under control? This had taken over half an hour and I do believe Christine is the only person to have seen the full transformation work its way through.

We left Pero looking surprised still, insisting that my dancing had been OK by him and had not put him out. Nevertheless his face had a mixed startled and puzzled expression on it. But on subsequent evenings I was welcomed and chauffeured back to Villa Giardino.

But if the day's medicine is past its shelf life for the day, and I am struggling at midnight, then it is unlikely to kick in. If I am not too tired I can try getting momentum with fast music, although doing this can hurt a lot since I am forcing my body to go through movements it is not wanting to do or physically set up for.

In particular when tired my legs tend to very bent at the knees and if I do not notice there is no way I will take off.

To really get moving my legs must be in a straight position when stopped, and I sometimes have to put as much effort into that as I do trying to get up a dancing speed. So of course as for elegance, you can forget it, now I am completely 'marionetted', static most of the time, coiled ready to go, but with no lift off. Then the occasional pulling of strings as I grotesquely do several steps of some skill, except there is no skill, just a lurching unbalanced ungainly series of staccato steps that as suddenly as they started come to a grinding halt Nevertheless, if I force the issue, I can sometimes get lift off, and once achieved, as long as I maintain a fair dancing pace, I can keep going indefinitely, or at least as long as I have energy, inclination and no complaints (Jasna likes us to sleep at night).

All this I can make work for me but I am still younger than most patients when they are first diagnosed so maybe the idea of a 70 year old suddenly attempting to be Gene Kelly from a zero rated recent dancing past is unlikely. Dancing is not exactly a transferable skill at a Parkinson's sufferer's typical age. And I have been dancing with increasing fervour for about 6 years now, time enough to become a moderate dancing act. Apart from being a bit fit, inspired and determined, you need to be thick-skinned and able to carry bruising with equanimity!

7.4 I COULD HAVE DANCED ALL NIGHT – MUSIC TO DANCE TO

At one extreme, when I get the chance to go and give seminars to students at residential courses, and there is the opportunity to dance in the evening (for which I have a speaker system for my iPod of impressive power and clarity) then I will be the first at the designated dancing area, and will dance virtually non-stop, subject to drink and comfort breaks, until everyone has gone to bed, sometimes four to five hours later. My personal preferences are for a mix of modern rock/pop/alternative and a variety of older material.

Some of the songs on my playlists are more or less the same speed throughout and these will generally be to provide relative moments of calm between some stormy dance tracks, or if really slow, to give me a cooling down period before stopping in the hope that when I stop I will not sweat profusely for too long. Examples of the former are

Twist by Goldfrapp

Teardrop by Massive Attack and

Get Down Saturday Night by Oliver Cheatham

And of the latter

Queer by Garbage

Some tracks are just very fast and these are either for fun when I am in full swing, or are called upon in desperation if I am off and cannot get started after several attempts. In the former case, they are clearly fun. In the latter case I can be quite desperate at this stage and I am risking some form of strain by deliberately 'throwing' my body at a song in the hopes that it will then keep itself going. If I am tired this is usually not a good idea because it can exhaust me quickly and then the whole point of dancing is lost and I may as well go to bed. However when it does work it's a great feeling that you have danced yourself out of control of the disease even though in too short a time I may be back. Examples of such tracks in are:

Hey U by Basement Jaxx (although slower for first half)

Four tracks by Jools Holland: Everybody needs someone to love; My country man; Roll this soul tonight; and especially Double O Boogie

Charmer by Kings of Leon

Most of the Muse tracks especially Showbiz and Hysteria

If You Wanna? by Parka is, which is not for the faint-hearted, so to speak!

My favourite types of song are what I call Wind-Up songs, which start slowly and gradually build up speed for ever (or so it seems). I thoroughly enjoy the challenge. Examples of such songs are:

Candela by Buena Vista Social Club

Shake That by Eminem featuring Nate Dogg (if bothered at all, which I doubt, I am sure Eminem will be pleased to hear that I love the beat but the lyrics are just distasteful).

Sorry by Madonna

Shania Twain's That Don't Impress Me Much

It's Raining Men by The Weather Girls ("so that each and every woman can find the perfect guy" – no chance!)

Other songs available are there because either I like them a lot whatever or they are mood songs.

No one playlist covers all the range, or if it did it would not be serving any useful purpose. So, for example, I can call on some classical music or easy listening such as:

Beethoven's 5th Symphony, the second to last parts (the first part has little novelty)

Beethoven's Piano Sonata Number 8, op13 "Pathetique"

West Side Story

Carmen

My tastes change quite rapidly as I get used to some songs and when there is no stimulation from playing them they are put aside. My iPod has over 8000 tracks on it, approximately 20% classical. Many tracks I have never heard yet, so I need never be stuck for variety.

Given all I have said about song familiarity, personal state of health, personal preferences and a need for a dynamically changing playlist to match your usage, clearly the songs mentioned in this book are meant to be indicative of styles of dance music and not direct recommendations.

7.5 THERE IS A TIME AND A PLACE

I am in the garden of Villa Giardino in Bol, Island Brac, Croatia and in preparation for writing this section I have just made sure I am moving properly with a 30 minute session ending in Mystic's old number *Ritmo De La Noche* (hardly anyone's favourite number, but a great beat). The owner of the hotel Christine is very understanding especially as her late husband Vinko, who was himself extraordinary as well as fun to chat with, had encouraged me last year at the Hotel to dance whenever and wherever I wanted. Vinko watched me in some of my wilder movements, looked bemused and mystified how I could dance like that, but insisted always on me continuing as much as I liked. I shall always remember him and that twinkle in his eye as he overcame his amazement and encouragingly waved me on. Little did I know that as he encouraged me in my fight with my illness, he was knowingly or not losing his personal battle with illness?

Another example of support is when people know of my condition and my personal dancing style for dealing with it. They are not only sympathetic (which to be honest is not much use to me) but they also spend time understanding why and what I need, and go out of their way to help me. The British Airways vignette in Chapter One for example is not just another example, it has been the forerunner of 6 to 7 long haul overnight flights where I have done a fair amount of dancing with not just the crew's permission but their encouragement. As already mentioned on one flight I was going well so I danced non-stop for four hours – what a way to make the journey not only not tedious but even a pleasure. All these long haul planes have been British Airways, and lately Virgin Atlantic but other carriers have allowed me to do some light dance work for short durations as well. Thank you all.

There is a cost though. Invariably when I tell people my Parkinson's disease story, they share with me some personal tragedy of their own, and this in my view is usually much worse than my current fate. I have two stories to tell, with the permission of the owners, one in a vignette called 'Really, let me tell you about ...' and another vignette called 'The Sign from God'.

There is a lot more unhappiness in the world than meets the eye.

Car parks, hotel foyers, people's homes, my and other people's offices, in private or in semi-public, if I am seizing up, dancing is my way out. So largely I take it. If I do not I usually regret it as my mobility gets worse.

What can I do to make my needs more acceptable? First in the next section I explain the problem and in the last section I propose a solution. Which is, of course, that everyone should dance. Then my dancing needs would not be seen as at best idiosyncratic.

7.6 JUDGEMENT AND UNDERSTANDING

We human beings see something and we try to make sense of it. If what we see is not within the sphere of normality that each individual seems to me to create for themselves about the world, then a variety of reactions are called upon.

To exaggerate to make a point:

The Really, Let Me Tell You About ... Vignette

As discussed in an earlier chapter, I defended the University in an Industrial Tribunal in 2004 after I retired and it was quite an experience. Readers will appreciate I like telling stories about myself (obviously the best stories after all!) and so a few weeks later I was at a social function sitting opposite a friend and a respected employee of a research grant awarding UK Government agency and started up with "I was a witness at an Industrial Tribunal ...". That was as far as I got. My friend cut in with "Were you, I have recently been to a Coroner's Court". How could she cut me off from my fantastic story to tell me something boring I thought? But I was wrong.

My friend had gone for a walk with her grown up son on some open land when in the distance they saw a car knock down a cyclist. They hurried over to the scene just in time to see the young teenage boy die in front of their eyes. Since my friend was the last adult to see the boy alive, she had to give evidence in a special court (called the Coroners Court in the U.K). This was bad enough, but the witness box faced the front row of the public part of the Court and there in the front row of the seating were the distraught parents of the dead boy.

After that story, my Industrial Tribunal experience suddenly seemed quite soft.

If what we are observing is not 'normal' and might be dangerous, we either get out of the way or if possible if the risk of doing so seems small kill it. Snakes and other reptiles, and insects readily fall into this category.

The Sign from God Vignette

A publisher who has been a friend of mine for I guess some 20 years gave me permission to tell this story. Some years ago when she was a single-parent student mother looking after her three children, her man walked out just as Easter approached. Clutching her banker's card she went to the bank for cash for Easter weekend to feed her and the children. The Bank in its majesty pointed out that she was overdrawn and confiscated her card. The fact that there were three children, a single mother and it was Easter weekend had nothing to do with banking rules.

She had had enough. She decided to commit suicide.

She set off to the pharmacy and purchased with her pitiful remaining coins as many Paracetemol as she could. Where to die? As a Christian, she decided that it would be appropriate if her final act on earth were to be in the Cathedral. So off she set armed and determined to die. But ...

This was the Twentieth Century, churches and cathedrals are particularly short of money, so when she arrived there was an admission charge. She had no money left, it all went on Paracetemol. She was not allowed in!

She turned, thought about it and at that moment decided God had intervened and stopped her killing herself. Therefore she should go back to her life and get on with it as best she could.

And now she is happily married, with grandchildren, and a top job, well respected, competent, intelligent and alive. And I am proud she sees me as her friend, and I am lucky to be in a position to consider her mine.

In war fear is so extreme that humans will kill each other viciously as a self-survival bloodlust is unleashed.

I am sure if there is a life on other planets and some of the citizens paid earth a visit, they had better convincingly and quickly let us know their peace seeking initiatives. Otherwise they will be killed as quickly as possible just in case they were coming to hurt us. Afterwards we would seek out their intentions, and if peaceful, we would apologise to their superiors from whence they came.

Some human cultures adopt a patriarchal authoritarian approach to organising its society, and so conformity is expected of its citizens. Some cultures prize individuality and in order to assist in this, a mass of products are available for a range of individualities. But, if you step outside the current range of commercialised individualities, then you could be a trend setter or more likely some sort of trouble maker or deviant or undesirable. Depending on the circumstances, the combination of people around and their prejudices, the general approach to a non-conformer appears to be at best to be formally civil, to judging them both in legal terms and non-legal as well, or at an extreme to vent some form of verbal abuse or even violence to this non-conforming individual. Racism is one example, when fear concerning the differences between nations or people's colour requires the different individual to be discriminated against.

So largely when I walk in public places and even more so when I dance, the general public if they show any interest at all (the majority do not) have a tendency on the whole to treat me with derision, contempt, irritation or sometimes the threat of physical violence can be sensed (only when dancing). Very rarely has someone bothered to find out if there is a reason for my behaviour.

An example of the threat of physical violence is the night club in the Hotel Croatia in Cavtat Croatia (see acknowledgements for further details) which is basically a bar with a disco floor and a DJ. The club is thinly populated and often when I dance there everyone except the staff dance – which is just me since I am the only customer. At first the bar staff were a little surprised but they have got used to me. If there are other customers I can tell that my fast dancing intimidates would be dancers, and even when I take a break (not really wishing to) for a couple of songs, this still does not encourage other dancers.

If the disco is unusually popular I can be faced with rival dancers, imitating my movements more grotesquely than even I manage to, or cutting across my dancing space. Sometimes people give me angry looks, or even dance threateningly close. In the year year 2007, a rather drunk Russian decided to dance with me, very closely whether I liked it or not. The first time the bar staff rushed across and pulled him away. The second time I left the disco altogether since there was no reason to endanger me or the bar staff when I could come back another day. Afterwards I told the bar staff why I dance and they are now much more than just protective

But when people know why I am nearly always wired up when I go out and move about, they become quite protective even though not dancing with me. To cover the second point first, I dance when I feel like it to suit me, so I cannot expect anybody else to do differently. Most people have no inclination to leap into silent dancing at all. So the support I get is not dancing with me (always an option) but being close by in a protective sort of way, showing solidarity with me. For example at a conference in 2007 there was an evening reception/dinner. There was also a group, a singer plus three musicians giving decent renderings of middle of the road songs. Since I had 'stiffened up' considerably I had to show my appreciation and so I started, cautiously slowly and speeding up. Half a dozen friends positioned themselves around me at a decent distance. Most people looked surprised or quizzical or irritated or made jokes with their friends if I was noticed by them. After half an hour I was joined by a female colleague from LSE and then after another 30 minutes there were 20 to 30 people dancing.

To end on another positive note I give you the 'Russian Norwegian Dancing' Vignette.

7.7 DANCING FOR ALL

Music helps me walk better (to a rhythm) and overcome my immobility by dancing to it. Exercise is good for Parkinson's sufferers, and dancing the way I do it is exercise. Music largely makes people happier and dancing unwinds people, releases the tensions of the day. So why are people not dancing more?

Even if you are fit, releasing the tensions of life, exercising and being sociable are recognised as generally beneficial. So everyone should get dancing. You may think you are not a good dancer; you have two left feet etc. Nonsense, if embarrassed then dance on your own as follows: Stand loose and get a feel for the music. As you get into the sound, staying loose, let your body move freely in any way it wants, swinging from side to side, twisting at the waist, whatever. When you get used to it you might want to move your feet at some later session. Over many sessions keep relaxing and 'going with' the music, by which I mean keep all your movements natural to you from what you hear.

Half an hour a day and you will be starting basic dancing sometime in the near future.

The Russian Norwegian Vignette

It was the last night of my holiday at Hotel Croatia Cavtat in 2006 and I was dancing in the Night Club just before closing at 3pm. There were two tables occupied by customers at that time and I had exchanged courtesies with both groups. I took it upon myself to invite both groups to join me on the dance floor and to my surprise they did. I was quite friendly with the DJ who after some dancing asked me how I had achieved this visually unusual dancing group. What he was referring to was the following:

One group was made up of four very young almost-dressed Russian girls and their English male 'friend'. The second group were from Northern Norway, three mature 'sensibly dressed' ladies and a male colleague. It is worth pointing out, in case I ever see any of them again that there were no unattractive females in the Night Club. The dancing consisted of the Norwegians dancing 'Abba' style to the music whatever it was, and the Russian girls simulated sexual intercourse with each other on the dance floor. And I danced quickly, gliding through the various dance renderings, avoiding enticement by either group.

Afterwards I spent half an hour chatting with the DJ and one of the two groups. Which group? Don't be silly, the Norwegians of course, I neither wished to be eaten alive nor divorced!!!

INVITED CONTRIBUTION: *DR P BAIN ON PARKINSON'S DISEASE*

Short Introduction
When I wrote in simple terms in section 1.6 what Parkinson's disease is, I promised that I would include a more technical version after I had told my story. I have told my story, and we have arrived at the point where Dr Bain's version is now presented. But although it is very technical, the technical jargon is used as a prop to a full review of what Parkinson's disease actually is. So I can only recommend that everyone reads this Special Guest Section, and passes the messages on to friends. This is an excellent piece of writing which succinctly puts the illness under the spotlight, discusses mental effects on patients and generally says all you need to know.

You can see how fortunate I am to have Dr Bain as my consultant. He ought to be a full Professor. But to be a professor, you not only need to do good work, but you must bring it to the right peoples' attention. Dr Bain has a great patient manner, gets good results, and by all the academic measures of performance should be a Professor. But in one respect he is too quiet, and the meek do not inherit the earth. So his employer has not been as aware of him as the average male promotional candidate, who usually has no problem to claim any success around him no matter how tenuous. Dr Bain will get there; it's just a matter of time

WHAT IS PARKINSON'S DISEASE?

By Dr Peter Bain, Reader & Honorary Consultant, Imperial College London

INTRODUCTION

Parkinson's disease (PD) can be understood from several different perspectives, the primary one being that lived by sufferers of the illness. However, Parkinson's disease is also felt by the families and friends of people with Parkinson's and observed by colleagues and casual acquaintances. As a neurologist, my day to day experience has come from the management of patients with PD, although my perceptions are also shaped by insights into the condition obtained by reading and writing papers and attending lectures on PD given by other experts. In this regard it is remarkable how quickly knowledge of the condition is evolving. Over the last decade there have been considerable advances in our understanding of the pathological processes underlying PD, the effects of these processes on patients and also advances in the medical and surgical treatment of the condition. I am optimistic that this progress will continue and even accelerate.

AGEING

Second by second, day by day we get older. So that by the fourth decade we are less physically active and learning new facts becomes more difficult. This slow but relentless erosion of our youthful prowess continues as the years roll bye. However, hopefully this is counterbalanced to some degree by the development of a more mature attitude and a broader sense of perspective, as life teaches us wisdom and compassion. Intriguingly mild

Parkinsonian signs develop with age in many people. A recent study, conducted in East Boston (U.S.A.), showed that 15% of the population aged 65-74, 30% aged 75-84 and 53% aged 85 years or more had mild Parkinsonian signs. These signs include deficits in gait and balance, stiffness, slowness of movement and tremors. The causes for these signs are not understood, they may reflect the ageing process itself, damage to the brain caused by cerebrovascular disease (the colloquial term for this being 'hardening of the arteries') or the development of a neurodegenerative disorder, for example true Parkinson's disease or Alzheimer's disease, or other factors. What is clear is that all these people do not fulfil current criteria for the diagnosis of Parkinson's disease, which is much rarer, affecting 0.2% of the overall population, 1% of people over 65 and 3% in those 75-85 years old.

THE PRE-DIAGNOSIS PHASE OF PARKINSON'S DISEASE

It is now widely appreciated that the processes causing Parkinson's disease start several years before patients present to their doctors with symptoms. This is called the pre-clinical or pre-diagnosis phase and has attracted considerable interest from the scientific community interested in developing therapies that could halt the disease process at this stage, before overt symptoms became apparent. These potential disease arresting or modifying therapies are termed 'neuroprotective agents' but alas no such agents have yet been shown to be effective in arresting the disease. In part this is because until recently it has been difficult to identify individuals prior to the diagnosis of Parkinson's disease actually being made and thus there was not a suitable cohort of people on whom to conduct therapeutic trials. However, this situation has now changed.

Over the last decade neurologists have learnt that this pre-clinical phase has an average duration of about 6 years and is characterised by several symptoms. These include deterioration in the person's sense of smell, the development of constipation and a phenomenon known as Rapid Eye Movement Sleep Behavioural Disorder (REMSBD). This consists of a tendency to have vivid (life-like) dreams, which can be enacted out and accompanied by shouting and thrashing out in sleep. This nocturnal behavioural disorder may disturb the spouse more than the sufferer and can be treated with a small dose of clonazepam. In addition in many instances patients report that they developed a frozen shoulder, weight loss or depression some years before the diagnosis of PD was made.

PRESENTATION WITH PARKINSON'S DISEASE

Eventually an individual will present to a doctor with the characteristic symptoms of Parkinson's disease. The most common being tremor or reduced dexterity in one hand. Typically, at the initial consultation, patients or their kin appreciate that they have slowed down, become a little less animated and more impassive or overtly depressed. Handwriting may have become smaller (micrographia), slower and more tremulous. Walking may be slightly less automatic and there may be a degree of consciousness involved in striding with one leg. The examining neurologist may detect some facial and vocal impassivity and perhaps a reduced rate of blinking. In the affected hand a tremor, stiffness (felt by the examiner as a cogwheel like resistance to passive movements of the patient's wrist) and slowness of fine finger movements (bradykinesia) may be apparent. A reduction in arm swing, during walking, on the patient's affected side is usually evident to the neurologist. Thus judged by its signs the condition is unilateral or predominantly unilateral at presentation, although in some cases the foot is affected prior to the arm. The tremors of Parkinson's disease are quite varied, the most characteristic (but rare) being a tremor that resembles rolling a pill in the fingers (termed 'a pill-rolling tremor'). More typically a tremor is seen in the fingers when they are resting or when held out stretched, respectively called rest and postural tremors. However about 20% of patients with PD do not have tremor. At this stage medical treatment is often not necessary, as disability is minimal, and the patient should be encouraged to remain mentally and physically active and take regular exercise. Attending pilates or yoga classes can also be helpful. The issue of when to tell the rest of the family and work colleagues about the diagnosis arises. Clearly, this matter should be considered on an individual basis but in my view being 'open' about the illnesses usually provides a sense of relief. Furthermore, if the patient holds a driving licence it is a legal requirement for them to inform the DVLA (Author's note: this is the Driver's Vehicle Licensing Centre in the U.K. – there will be similar agencies in many countries) about the diagnosis of PD. Subsequently, after some simple paperwork that individual is nearly always allowed to continue driving, subject to periodic review. It is also important to inform one's insurers about the illness, in order for the relevant policies to remain valid.

Although medical treatment may not be necessary at the time of diagnosis depression should be treated because it is the major determinant of quality of life for people with Parkinson's disease. Treatment of depression by counselling, an antidepressant or both can be very helpful. In addition it is important that arrangements are made so that a newly diagnosed person with PD is followed up regularly by a physician with an interest in the condition, typically at 3 to 6 monthly intervals, so that the situation is regularly reviewed and that person feels supported. If the person is disabled by the condition symptomatic medical treatment should be introduced as necessary. The widely held 'impression' that delaying the introduction of treatment for Parkinson's disease is advantageous to the sufferer and that medication should be withheld for as long as possible has little to support it and is the cause of considerable and unnecessary suffering. This 'early' phase of Parkinson's can last for several months to many years and it is important to appreciate that the condition is very diverse and that individual's experiences vary immensely. Thus what follows is merely a sketch of the illness.

THE EARLY STAGES OF PARKINSON'S DISEASE (WITHIN 5 YEARS OF DIAGNOSIS)

Left untreated the main symptoms of PD gradually increase in severity. The tremor becomes more persistent, may spread from the fingers up the arm and then, typically after 3 years, to the ipsilateral leg. The slowness of movement (bradykinesia) and stiffness (rigidity) increase, although most activities of daily living can be accomplished, albeit somewhat more slowly. Difficulties with buttons and fine manual tasks may become evident.

Fortunately, effective medical treatment is available. The main issue is whether to take a levodopa preparation (Madopar®, Sinemet®, Stalevo®) or to use another class of drug, in order to delay the introduction of levodopa. These drugs include mono-amine oxidase type B (MAO-B) inhibitors (selegiline or rasagiline), non-ergot direct acting dopamine agonists (ropinirole, pramipexole, rotigotine), anti-cholinergics (orphenadrine, trihexyphenidyl, procyclidine, benztropine) or amantadine.

The introduction of a levodopa preparation is predominantly a question of timing. The advantage of using levodopa early is that it is more effective than the other classes of drug used. The disadvantage is that about 50% of patients treated with levodopa for 5 years develop involuntary movements (dyskinesias) and motor fluctuations, in which the treatment cuts out more abruptly, causing an 'off' period in which the signs and symptoms of PD become more evident. It is now appreciated that these complications of levodopa therapy are caused by the way the drug is delivered. If levodopa is delivered in a pulsatile way involuntary movements and motor fluctuations occur. If the drug can be given in a constant way these problems are minimized. The ideal delivery of levodopa would thus provide continuous dopaminergic stimulation rather than pulsatile stimulation. As the direct acting dopamine agonist and MAO-B inhibitor classes of drugs have longer half-lives than levodopa, these drugs are preferred to levodopa when medical therapy is initiated in young people, as treatment may be necessary for several decades. On empirical grounds most experts start patients aged 70 or more on levodopa but consider using the other classes of drug first for patients under 65. The pros and cons of each approach are usually discussed carefully with patients, particularly those in the intermediate (65-70) age group.

In general with medical treatment very good control of the symptoms can be achieved and the early part of this stage is often referred to as the 'honeymoon' period. However, medication does not prevent progression of the underlying disease process, so that typically about 7 years after diagnosis signs become manifest in the opposite arm and leg, albeit usually more mildly than on the initially affected side. Even so with gradually escalating therapy, often involving a combination of medical treatments, it is usually possible to control the cardinal symptoms of the condition, namely rigidity, slowness of movement and tremors, so that patients remain active.

THE MID STAGES OF PARKINSON'S DISEASE (5-15 YEARS FROM DIAGNOSIS)

The mid stages of the illness have been the period for most of the major developments in the treatment of Parkinson's disease that have occurred over the last two decades. In particular the use of adjunctive treatment to levodopa with a MAO-B inhibitor (rasagiline or selegiline) or a catechol-O-methyl transferase inhibitor (entacapone or tolcapone) have ameliorated the wearing off phenomena to some degree, so that the effect of each levodopa tablet is potentiated and prolonged. As a result the 'off' periods in which patients feel down, anxious and 'parkinsonian' (because of increased rigidity, tremor and bradykinesia) are reduced or shortened. In addition the use of quick acting, dispersible, levodopa or apomorphine rescue injections have helped to 'kick-start' the patient's day and also rescue them from a severe 'off' period. More recently it has become appreciated that movement itself has a similar effect so that when a patient feels an 'off' period coming on, getting up and moving about can help prevent it or reduce its severity. Thus movement improves the symptoms of parkinsonism. Consequently, it is imperative that people with Parkinson's disease remain active and take regular exercise.

Involuntary movements (dyskinesias) become more of an issue during the mid stages of Parkinson's disease. These involuntary movements tend to occur during the peak, beneficial, effect of dopaminergic treatment. They are often mild and well tolerated by patients and considered preferable to an 'off' period, although spouses and family may find the movements and thus the patient more irritating. Frequently, dyskinesias appear when the patient is mentally engaged or anxious, for example when hurrying to go out to a social event, and are often more intrusive in the afternoon compared to morning. To some extent relaxation ameliorates dyskinesia. In some instances these involuntary movements can become very intrusive and may become 'diphasic' appearing when the medication begins to take effect and also begins to wear off. Sometimes tailoring the medication, using lower doses of levodopa more frequently, or introducing the anti-dyskinesia drug amantadine can help.

However, if in spite of optimal medical treatment dyskinesias and/or wearing off phenomena dominate the patient's day recourse to more advanced technological solutions is required. These include using an apomorphine infusion pump, a Duodopa® pump or recourse to stereotactic neurosurgery. Any one of these treatments can induce a considerable reduction in the severity and duration of dyskinesias and the 'off' periods during the day, with concomitant improvements in the individual's quality of life.

The apomorphine pump, infuses an injectable dopamine agonist (apomorphine – which has no relationship to morphine) at a set flow rate under the skin through a small needle. The pump can be worn for the waking day or all day and night. This provides more constant dopaminergic stimulation, which gradually ameliorates the dyskinesias and 'off' periods caused by the pulsatile delivery of levodopa produced by tablets. Similarly a Duodopa® pump infuses a gel form of levodopa into part of the small intestine via a tube inserted through the stomach. Again this creates a more stable level of levodopa in the blood and thus more constant dopaminergic stimulation, producing similar benefits to apomorphine.

Alternatively stereotactic surgery can be performed to alleviate dyskinesia and improve 'off' periods if necessary. In addition severe tremor that cannot be controlled by medication can be more or less abolished. This form of surgery involves inserting a probe deep into the brain in order to modulate abnormal activity in brain circuitry that is in turn inducing symptoms. Surgery is performed on the right side of the brain to control left sided symptoms and vice versa. Bilateral surgery can be performed if symptoms affect both sides of the patient's body. The major risks of this type of surgery are a 1 in 1000 risk of death and a 1 in 100 risk of a stroke, which might produce weakness or numbness down one side of the body or speech deficits. However in over 95% of cases stereotactic surgery is helpful for appropriate patients. However, there are rigorous selection criteria that are in place to maximise benefit to those who have surgery and minimise disappointing results. There are currently two types of mainstream stereotactic surgical procedure carried out. One involves making a lesion, literally burning a small hole in the brain, to damage the abnormally active brain circuit. The second involves leaving a probe in the brain, which is connected by wires under the skin to a small battery driven pacemaker that is usually buried under the collar bone. This is known as deep brain stimulation. Both techniques are effective but deep brain stimulation appears to be slightly safer particularly when bilateral surgery is undertaken. To complicate matters there are several different sites within the brain that can be targeted by surgery, depending on the patient's most intrusive symptoms. However, presently the subthalamic nucleus is the preferred site for deep brain stimulation and over 40,000 of these procedures have now been carried out world-wide.

THE LATE STAGES OF PARKINSON'S DISEASE (15-25 YEARS FROM DIAGNOSIS)

About 15 to 25 years after diagnosis the patient enters the later stages of Parkinson's disease. It is worth reflecting that given that the typical age of onset of PD is between

60 to 65 years, the patient would now be in their eighth or ninth decade and affected by all the frailties associated with old age that are common to all humanity in addition to Parkinson's disease.

Now the illness becomes dominated by what are termed 'non-dopaminergic' features. Many of the symptoms of early to mid stage Parkinson's disease respond well to dopaminergic treatment. However, there is a gradual accrual of symptoms that are independent of dopamine. These can include constipation, bladder dysfunction, poor temperature regulation, drooling saliva, speech deficits, poor blood pressure control, fragmented sleep, deterioration in gait with instability and falls and cognitive decline, confusion, hallucinations or dementia. At this stage Parkinson's patients need support from their family or carers or are in a nursing home. Fortunately, much of current research is aimed at finding solutions to these symptoms.

THE CAUSES OF PARKINSON'S DISEASE

The causes of Parkinson's disease are not currently understood, although there has been considerable progress in our understanding of the nature of the illness in recent years. It is classified as a neurodegenerative illness, which implies that neural tissue degenerates. It would perhaps be more accurate to term it a neuroprogressive disease, as it affects neural tissue in a slowly progressive way. However, what triggers the start of this process is not known. There are some epidemiological clues in that rural residence, farming, pesticide exposure and drinking water from wells are all risk factors for the condition. Conversely, cigarette smoking and drinking coffee are associated with a decreased risk of developing PD, even when adjusted for the detrimental effects of smoking on general health. However, care must be exercised in interpreting this information as causal, as it may be that people with certain personality traits are more inclined to smoke or drink coffee and such personalities may reflect an intrinsic quality that reduces the risk of developing PD.

Studies of twins have not given clear results, although several causative genetic abnormalities have now been identified, predominantly for younger onset patients with rare forms of parkinsonism. These include the dominantly inherited α-Synuclein and recessively inherited Parkin, DJ-1, and PINK 1 mutations. However, in typical sporadic Parkinson's disease with an onset age of greater than 60 years genetic mutations are rare, accounting for less than 5% of cases. In this regard mutations in the LRRK2 gene cause about 1% of sporadic PD cases. Presently research is focussing on 'susceptibility genes', namely genetic abnormalities or variants of normal genes that are not causal but slightly increase an individual's risk of developing PD.

Even if the results of genetic studies have been somewhat disappointing in terms of establishing a cause for Parkinson's disease in most sufferers, they have provided some useful insights into the biochemical faults present in the illness. For example, neuropathologists have demonstrated in brains obtained from patients who had parkinsonism caused by a mutation in the α-Synuclein gene that a protein called α-Synuclein is laid down in aggregates within affected brain cells. Furthermore, this protein is a constituent of an abnormal structure present within certain brain cells of people with PD known as the 'Lewy body' (named after the German pathologist who identified this structure by microscopy), which is the hallmark of Parkinson's disease pathology. By looking at the distribution of α-Synuclein (and thus Lewy bodies) in brains, obtained post-mortem from serially more affected patients with PD, there appears to be a gradual progression of α-Synuclein deposition from the brainstem and olfactory nuclei, through the midbrain to the cerebral cortex as the disease progresses. This is known as 'Braak staging' and in simple terms appears to indicate that the pathology causing PD rises up the brain in several stages. However, this hypothesis is still controversial and may be rather too simplistic.

Within cells are mitochondria, small structures that are predominantly involved in energy production. A defect in the mitochondria (mitochondrial complex 1 deficiency) has been found in Parkinson's disease and it is thought that this may make cells more vulnerable to a process called 'oxidative stress', in which free radicals damage cells. A free radical is a molecule with one or more unpaired electrons that have a tendency to extract electrons from other molecular structures. Perhaps this process might trigger cell damage and the subsequent pathological changes apparent in specific areas of the brain in Parkinson's disease. As a result anti-oxidant vitamins have been advocated for patients with PD, including co-enzyme Q10, Enada NADH, Vitamin A, C and E. However, there is presently no proof that these vitamins are effective in reducing the rate of progression of the illness, although one trial involving co-enzyme Q10 has shown some positive results.

Whatever triggers the onset of Parkinson's disease the resulting damage, indicated by the presence of Lewy bodies, can eventually be found in numerous locations within the brain, spinal cord, and peripheral sympathetic ganglia and plexuses. It is well established that the characteristic clinical signs of Parkinson's disease, tremor, rigidity and slowness of movement, do not develop until 50% of the brain cells within a small region of the brain termed the substantia nigra (literally 'the black substance') have died and the level of dopamine, a chemical transmitter produced by these cells, has been reduced by 80% in an area called the striatum. The cells in the substantia nigra contain melanin, which is black, and project to the striatum. It is as a consequence of this dopamine depletion that dopaminergic therapies are able to provide symptomatic relief by supplementing the deficient dopamine state caused by the disease. It is remarkable that that levodopa, a simple chemical, has for three decades, transformed the lives of millions of people with Parkinson's disease throughout the world.

LIFE AND PARKINSON'S DISEASE

In the end it is 'ashes to ashes and dust to dust' for all of us. Living through Parkinson's disease is a subjective and unique experience, which has been made much more tolerable by treatment and will in future be made better still. Having had more than twenty years experience of treating people with Parkinson's disease I have appreciated that those patients who remain mentally, physically and socially active do well. My advice to people with PD is to *be a moving target and not a sitting duck*. I feel and hope that further breakthroughs in the treatment of Parkinson's disease are tantalizingly close and I am sure that remaining optimistic is a major step towards coping with this illness.

THE SEVEN BOOK AUTOBIOGRAPHY

1. Living with Parkinson's disease: Shake, Rattle and Roll

Even if this, my first autobiographical book is not successful (that is does not sell many copies) I still intend to write the following two titles (numbers 2 and 3 below) which are in themselves potentially commercial. If this Parkinson's disease book is commercially successful, then I anticipate there may be interest in four more books I could write. The four books might help a variety of people with their lives, or just be entertaining, or both. The four books are numbered 4 to 7 as listed below.

2. How I Supervise My PhD Students

A guide on how to supervise PhDs based on experiential material I have collected from the successful supervision of 55 students at the time of writing. The material has already been tested through seven one hour seminars that I often give on the subject.

3. The 105 Minute Guide to Working for Life: The Essential Airplane Book

Which I believe should have two alternative titles

'Paul's Laws' and

'The Pick Me Up Put Me Down Book'

Paul's Laws is a collection of my observations about people and systems that I have collected in moments of boredom on committees, meetings etc. The observations are cast as my 'Laws', hopefully humorous descriptions of how life really works.

4. An Ordinary Childhood

I have at least two siblings, three half-siblings, two step-siblings, and two common law siblings. I have 9 siblings of one sort or another, a mother, a common law mum and a step-mother. But it was ordinary to me – after all, it was the only childhood I had! The book covers my life from pre-birth to being a University student.

5. Lucky Ray

A modern view of a University career, from lecturer to Vice-Chancellor, in contrast to the starting of an academic career as portrayed in 'Lucky Jim' by Kingsley Amis. This book covers the professional part of my career, and whilst written in my usual humorous style, will have lots of advice for potential and actual academics. Anyone wanting to understand the academic world will also appreciate this book.

6. Popular Delusions

There are many views of life held in common which turn out to be delusions when examined properly. This book covers seven of them, describing the myths around them, and how to handle them more appropriately. The views are on the subjects of
change
    time or time management

quality
selfishness: self-absorption and external vision; self-promotion
courage and fear
solving problems (intelligent thinking)
systems and systemic thinking
health and wealth

7. Leading and Managing People: The LAMP Approach

The seventh and last book in the series is based on my experience as an academic manager. From what I have seen in a variety of organisations, the lessons are universally applicable. Especially because Higher Education is a large competitive business with commercial restrictions that private enterprise would have difficulty with. The topics covered are

Respect
Delegate and Defend
Responsibility and Reward
Quality Assurance In, Quality Assuredly Out
The Obvious Things Turn Out To Be Obviously Wrong
Strategy is "What Do You Want To Be?"
Exercising Control Leads to Loss of Control.

ACKNOWLEDGEMENTS

I have written this section to go last in the book so that when it is read a full appreciation of the people in my story can be gained. There are also many lessons to be drawn from my acknowledgements and some of these I will highlight. My family come first, as they should in all matters. My medical supporters follow on, and then Carole Bromley my secretary and Tillal Eldabi from Brunel University. It would not be possible to list all the people at Brunel University and at the LSE who have helped me without forgetting a name or two, so I hope everyone will accept this blanket thanks to you all.

I cannot rank my other carers, they all provide support for me in different walks of life and they all do so exceedingly well. Many people help and have helped me in the latter and the fact that so many are not mentioned by name is not indicative of my view of their contribution, nor have I forgotten them, merely that I have be aware of the readers' patience and not be exhaustive. Many people have of course already been named in the main text.

These acknowledgements are, then, about the people central to my life (my near family) and those people who directly contributed to the progress of this book. Although Jasna my wife has already been discussed twice (sections 2.5 and 4.6) I start with her. Jasna has lived with my Parkinson's disease almost as much as I have and so I wish to give her due recognition.

JASNA
Clearly my first and greatest thanks must go to my wife Jasna. Jasna is my wife, companion, lover, partner, carer,

mistress, confidant, homemaker, intellect, and beauty, open and honest and full-time Ray improver. No one deserves so much, but fortunately she loves me, so I receive it. I have had such good fortune in finding and partnering Jasna, a major factor in my ability to live with Parkinson's disease. For the first 2½ years since diagnosis she carried me single-handed. She has largely done much the same since I came out. She has suffered far more than anyone else, a fact largely unappreciated by our many professional and personal relationships I regret to say. My love for her is persistent and all pervasive.

MY CHILDREN AND GRANDCHILDREN

My two children are in good health, and are financially sound. I am very lucky, no father could ask for more. When Ruth was born in 1973 I realised that the love of a parent for a child is inherently far greater than the love of a child for a parent. Ruth's mother says I spent hours just staring at Ruth when she was born, I was besotted with her. I still am I have to admit.

My son Benjamin was born in 1977 and with his arrival, any ideas we held that we knew how to bring up children were quickly dispelled. Benjamin was liable to be hyperactive, requiring lots of physical activity to keep him occupied. But like his sister, he and she may or may not do as I might do in some circumstances, but they both have my unreserved love and admiration. Fathers are traditionally softer with their daughters than their sons, but this should not be confused with loving them differently whatever outward appearances might seem.

Ruth has provide me with three grand children, non-identical twin boys Phoenix and Elliot born in 2002, and

Evelyn who was born in 2008. Phoenix is a linguistically talented internally focussed individual, intensely dedicated to whatever he is interested in and rather oblivious of the outside world. Elliot is externally focussed, conscious of his surroundings, eager for attention and interested in making things work. He has a passion for Evelyn, kissing her frequently. Neither of the twins is aware of who will be in charge when Evelyn is about two or so. The grandchildren are a joy to me; I love to see them when possible.

Generally speaking I do not find new born babies particularly interesting, except for the arrival of my children mentioned above. When the twins were born I went to see two babies and was amazed when I was taken by them in the same way as I was with my children. The twins and Evelyn were instantly an extremely important part of my life, treasures no matter what else is happening to me. I look forward to the chance to see them mature into adults. And who knows, maybe I will find out in due course if great grandchildren have the same effect!

MY FATHER AND MY SIBLINGS

My father or Dad was born in 1920. He is still going strong, looking after his wife who is 25 years younger and has Multiple Sclerosis. Dad is always looking to the future, planning a variety of activity. He has recently mentioned the idea that he may not have long to live, which he worries about because he has "25 years worth of things still to do"! What an approach to life, I am lucky to have his genes. He worries about me and treats me as though I am relatively physically impaired compared to him!

My brother David and sister Mary keep a watchful eye on me; I am still the wounded champion, able to give advice whenever they ask. The three of us are nearly all retired (if I can ever understand such an idea) and I am sure we shall be even more mutually supportive.

MY MEDICAL SUPPORT

My neurologist Dr Peter Bain of Charing Cross Hospital and Cromwell Road Hospital is brilliant. He is quiet and unassuming and so has been consistently promoted incredulously late in his career in academia because as Oscar Wilde said:

> *"In unimportant matters in life, style is more important than substance, and in important matters in life, style is more important than substance."*

From my point of view as his patient give me his substance any day. And I rather admire his honest, direct passionate style too. I am one of my consultants best patients he informs me. After I had been told this many times I asked him why? You don't understand he answered, many of my patients are so miserable! For my part it is always a pleasure to see him, and I have complete trust in his knowledge and advice, which is rapidly adaptive to individualistic medical responses whether good or bad.

Because of the way healthcare is funded in the U.K my medication requirements put a great burden on the budget of my doctor (or general practitioner as they are called in the U.K.) both in terms of medication and in terms of hospital tests to check out reported side effects of my medication as they become reported. Dr Ewa Robinska is to be congratulated on the exemplary way she runs her surgery and the friendliness with which I am treated in spite of the expense! Dr Sillitoe is my registered doctor in the practice and she takes 'patient' care of me. Dr Warren, a previous member of the practice, is the white faced doctor in the story in the Preface: she helped me enormously in my depression period. The nurses and support staff at the practice all contribute to the professional caring efficiency of the practice. If there are patients who are unhappy with the practice, then their unhappiness is due to themselves and not the practice.

I believe in supporting local shops where practicable, and until recently I was fortunate to have as my pharmacist Dipak Patel, who ran the Kansett Pharmacy in Horn Lane Acton with several members of his family. He went out of his way to assist me, including finding medication that is packed in a way that I can use myself.

MY SUPPORT AT BRUNEL UNIVERSITY

On the professional side I have a secretary Carole Bromley looking after me and my diary at Brunel University, a full-time job only if you are any good at it. Carole worked for me first in 2003 as a temp. She can appear to be not with it and just a 'dumb blonde', but a little observation easily uncovers greater depth. Carole is a white witch with some unusual attributes. She doesn't do stress as she once put it, and is the cat who thinks it can look at the King (she has no concept of status, just ability and sense). Carole tries very hard to fix my going-home departure time by using her persuasive skills on my appointees to only spend so many minutes with me She deals with all the flack when I am not on time or do not turn up. Car parking, taxi booking, negotiating appointments, helping people get help from me, sorting out my emails and responding too many of them for me, similarly for correspondence, are all part of her every day remit.

But she is also proactive, suggesting that some colleagues in Brunel might like to invite me to give some seminars, negotiating the times and place, ensuring the right equipment, some water, handouts are all available and escorting me there to ensure timely arrival or holding the fort if I am late. Similarly the local and travel arrangements for external talks.

Ordering supplies, serving endless drinks, preparing my room appropriately (for example for when I chair PhD examinations, always in my office), keeping telephone communications with me, being available for a call or email from wherever I am even on holiday, calming people down who misunderstand what I am attempting to do: the list seems endless. When I am asked whether she could do some other work as well as look after me, my response is yes if the benefits would exceed my lower contribution because I am supported less. I know it sounds like emotional blackmail, but it happens to be also true that my contribution is a function of this support.

Carole is also a fairly unique character, a sense of humour (when things are going wrong she announces she is "having a blonde day today"). Although I do not know what to make of her witchcraft, I am sure she has some abilities beyond my comprehension, and since I know that what I do not know far exceeds my little knowledge, she comes into the unknown region comfortably for me. We have worked together a little on this and will continue to do so. Having watched me write this book, Carole decided to do the same, which she published two to thre months ahead of me. I have written a Foreword to the book, and the book is Carole Bromley (2009) *The Living Spirit: One Woman's Battle Amongst Ghosts, Spirits and the Living* Authorhouse, Milton Keynes.

Tillal Eldabi came to Brunel University as an MSc student of mine in 1993 from the Sudan, stayed around by any means possible to do his PhD, joined the Department's lecturing staff and recently was appointed Senior Lecturer in the Brunel Business School. He is the owner of the best ever response I have ever heard when during his PhD days I put him under pressure to tell me when I might expect to receive something from him. Relentlessly I sought an answer as he prevaricated until he killed the conversation dead with the breathtaking answer *"probably soon!"* Tillal keeps a watching brief on my health and professional activities, sorts out technical submission requirements for me for conferences and journals and even travels with me to seminars to give me support. Tillal is the best example of support given me by my ex-students for which I am grateful but this is not the book to go through them all (How I Supervise My PhD Students will be the book to do that).

MY FINANCIAL ADVISER

I have described in section 6.3 how the intervention of my financial advisor had on every occasion turned a problem into a solution. If you send your details to me on my website (www.rayjpaul.com) I will forward them to him.

WHERE I WROTE THE BOOK

THE VILLA GIARDINO

This book was conceived of in 2003, but the major chapter content planning and some of the writing took place at a delightful privately run hotel called Villa Giardino. Breakfast on the front garden terrace, dinner weather permitting in the back garden with its outdoor kitchen (excellent cooking in the 'Villa Giardino Canopy Giardino'), peace and tranquillity with a non-obtrusive service, set in a hillside residence at Bol on the island of Brac, Croatia. Each visit has been more productive for this book than any other holiday. In particular, the emotional strength to essentially write Chapter Two was only found, after two other attempts, on my 2006 visit.

My thanks go to Christine and Vinko Gratelli, the hotel owners, and their staff particularly the ever-helpful Aida. Every person has a 'story' to tell I have found. Christine and Vinko had a vision, the garden hotel, which they made into reality with considerable effort. They have had a turbulent professional lifestyle. The third member of the hotel family, Aida, joined the hotel over 14 years ago for a temporary summer job, but the Bosnian War took away her probable partner and the will to go back to Bosnia. In spite of this, they have all been exceptionally kind to me in many ways not warranted by me: garden dancing; and looking after my sustenance above and beyond the call of duty. They are all hard working honest and kind and I only wish a larger proportion of such people populated the world.

Vinko died in April 2007. He lies buried in the monastery churchyard overlooking Bol harbour. Whilst

Vinko is a great loss to many, and of course especially to Christine, one can feel his presence in the churchyard, keeping his eye on the town he was born in and always loved. And then there is Villa Giardino, a magnificent living reminder of a vision put into action and still maintained by the other half of the visionary couple Christine. As I have said elsewhere, people who mean something to you do not die, they live on inside you. Vinko easily comes to mind for me, larger than life still.

Vinko was not particularly proficient in English, but that did not stop him trying with me. On one occasion I successfully asked him after he had been in the garden serving 'special' guests until 2am, and then getting up at 6am, how he managed to do with so little sleep? He said in reply, with that particular Vinko twinkle in his eye "I sleep quickly!" What an answer, I quote him to this day. The twinkle, his caring nature, his energy, and his willingness to sort things out all made him Vinko.

For those seeking a garden oasis refuge from the modern world, the telephone number of Villa Giardino is ++ 385 21 635 900

THE HOTEL CROATIA, CAVTAT

Jasna and I met at a conference at the Hotel Croatia, Cavtat near Dubrovnik in 1988. We have regularly holidayed there every year except for the war years which resulted in the breakup of Yugoslavia. We are well known by many of the staff who greet us as old friends every year. This book has been partially written on some of these visits and the ambience and helpfulness of everyone in the hotel has encouraged and inspired me. The Night Club has seen me as a regular visitor in recent years since my dancing has become such a passion. The Night Club was not open in 2009 unfortunately. Many times I have danced solo for an hour or more with mixed reactions from other customers, but only support from the staff.

We have also been exceptionally well supported and listened to by the hotel's marketing manager Maria Šebalj. Maria has coffee with us every visit in spite of being extremely busy, and asks us for our views. Although like most people she prefers praise to criticism, she listens to our open and honest comments and we get the impression that they have an effect on her contribution to the running of the hotel. The hotel is very lucky to have her and we are very lucky to have her as a friend.

LEUT, FISH RESTAURANT

When staying at Hotel Croatia, Cavtat, we sometimes eat out for a change, and our favourite restaurant in Cavtat is Leut. Leut was opened in 1971 and is owned by Ivo Bobić, a lively outward looking local boy (with a passion for shirts, collar size 42cm) who pays attention to his customers needs and each year introduces some new aspect to the restaurant, which is perfectly located in the centre of town on the edge of the sea. In the early days of writing the book, much of the planning for the book was conducted over a delicious slow meal at Leut, and subsequently much text checking has been undertaken in similar delightful circumstances.

All the staff at Leut are friendly and well trained, but there is one waiter in particular, Tony Mehmet, whose advice over choice of menu is almost always excellent. The meal may turn out to be above the average price, but this is made up for by its quality and taste.